DATE DUE

RADAR AND RADAR
TECHNIQUES

Introduction to
RADAR AND RADAR
TECHNIQUES

by

DENIS TAYLOR
M.Sc., Ph.D., M.I.E.E., F.Inst.P.

Faculty of Engineering, University College, Nairobi, formerly Head of Electronics Division, Atomic Energy Research Establishment, Harwell, and one time Superintendent Scientist, Telecommunications Research Establishment (since renamed Royal Radar Establishment), Malvern.

PHILOSOPHICAL LIBRARY INC.

15 EAST FORTIETH STREET

NEW YORK 16, N.Y.

Published 1967 by Philosophical Library Inc.,
15 East 40th Street, New York 16, N.Y.

Printed in Great Britain for Philosophical Library by
The Whitefriars Press Ltd., London and Tonbridge.

CONTENTS

LIST OF PLATES

(Between pages 54 and 55)

PREFACE

This book tells the story of radar, its development and use during the war and the uses that have been made of radar and radar techniques since the war. It discusses scientific and technical matters, but in a way suitable for assimilation by the general reader. No knowledge of mathematics or radio theory is assumed, and it is hoped that the book will form suitable reading matter for sixth-form students in our schools, both on the science and the arts side.

The preparation of this book has naturally benefited from the work done on my earlier and more learned publication, *Principles of Radar* published by the Cambridge University Press in 1948, although this latter was a book written for postgraduate students and contained a fair amount of mathematics. I am therefore greatly indebted to the Syndics of the Cambridge University Press, who have been very generous in allowing me to use material originally prepared for the *Principles of Radar* publication.

Naturally in a book of this size it has been impossible to give a comprehensive account of every aspect of radar, and in the case of the more modern matters, security restrictions have, of course, prevented me from providing full details. Nevertheless, it is hoped that my readers will agree that I have given a reasonably balanced account of the war-time developments with a fair indication of the way in which radar and the exploitation of radar techniques are affecting our modern world. Throughout, the treatment is that of relating the operational requirement to the scientific possibilities, and while the principles are explained together with a certain amount of the historical development, no attempt is made to give precise descriptions of the radar equipments considered. This is not considered appropriate in a book of this sort and not consistent with the objective of producing a really readable account of the developments.

I am indebted to a number of organisations who have allowed me to make use of illustrations or photographs, among whom must be mentioned the Royal Radar Establishment (Ministry of Aviation) and Manchester University.

DENIS TAYLOR

CHAPTER ONE

INTRODUCTION

HISTORICAL DEVELOPMENT

Radar, which can be simply described as the science of locating distant objects by radio, had its beginnings in the very early days of radio. Thus, the scattering of radio waves by material objects—a fundamental process in radar—was first observed by Hertz in his classical experiments conducted in 1886 demonstrating the existence of electromagnetic waves, i.e. radio waves. It is interesting, looking back, that the suggestion has been made on many occasions since this date that such scattering might be used for the actual location of distant objects. In fact, the first use of this scattering (or reflection) phenomena was that by Appleton and Barnett working at Cambridge University, who in 1924 used it to determine the height of the reflecting regions of the upper atmosphere. They employed what we call a frequency modulation method. In this method the transmitted frequency is increased linearly at a definite rate. The wave returned from the ionosphere* at a range r is delayed by a time interval $2r/c$, where c is the velocity of the radio waves. The latter wave therefore differs in frequency from the wave then being transmitted upwards, and the two waves incident on the receiver—the wave received directly from the transmitter (sometimes called the 'ground' wave) and the wave received after reflection at the ionosphere (the 'reflected' wave)—interfere, and beats result. By measuring this beat frequency, Appleton and Barnett were able to measure the range (r) of the ionosphere. This method has given good results, but for some purposes a variation of the method due to the American physicists Breit and Tuve is preferred. This method, which was introduced in 1925, uses amplitude modulation. In their experiments Briet and Tuve radiated pulses of 1/1000th second duration in a vertical direction, which after

---

* Ultraviolet radiation from the sun ionises the outermost part of the earth's atmosphere and liberates free electrons. These electrons may modify the refractive index of the atmosphere for radio waves and that part of the atmosphere where their effect is important is called the ionosphere. It extends from a height of about 60 km upwards to the outer fringes of the atmosphere.

reflection at the ionosphere were received at a receiver located in a position adjacent to the transmitter. The time of transit of the radio waves being constant and known, a direct determination was possible of the range of the ionosphere. It may be noted that if r is the range of the ionosphere, and t is the time of transit, then $t = 2r/c$, where c is again the velocity of the radio waves. The velocity c is equal to 186,000 miles per second. It follows therefore that every microsecond* of delay is equivalent to 0·186 mile.†

It is usual to display the reflected pulses on a cathode-ray tube time-base, and deduce the delay, and hence the range, from the distance the cathode-ray tube spot had moved across the screen. Figure 1 illustrates this method.

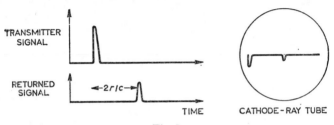

Fig. 1.

The particular advantage of the pulse method, which has led to its general adoption in preference but not to the exclusion of the frequency modulation method, arises when more than one reflecting object is present. Whereas the pulse method gives one or more clearly resolved echoes from objects at different ranges at the corresponding points on the time-base, the frequency modulation method gives only a complicated 'beats' waveform requiring special analysis to resolve it into its components.

The first reported observation on the reception of radio waves scattered by actual aircraft in flight was made in 1932 by British Post Office engineers, but they regarded this as 'interference' and failed to realise its possibilities.

In the United Kingdom the emergence of radar as a means of detecting and locating aircraft in flight came about largely as a

* A microsecond is a millionth part, i.e. 1/10⁶ of a second.

† Using echo delay = $2r/c$, the delay is approximately 10·7 microseconds per mile.

result of a carefully planned policy. It had been recognised that in war at least twenty minutes warning of the approach of enemy aircraft was necessary—otherwise all forms of defence were useless. As a result of inspired action by Wimperis, then Director of Scientific Research at the Air Ministry, a committee of scientists was set up to investigate the problems of defence against air attack. The committee was under the chairmanship of Sir Henry Tizard, and under his vigorous leadership the committee quickly defined the problems and began to consider possible solutions. One solution proposed by Watson-Watt (now Sir Robert Watson-Watt) attracted particular attention. Watson-Watt, who was then Superintendent of the Radio Department of the National Physical Laboratory, put together his experience of the pulse method of investigating the ionosphere and his knowledge of the observation of the reflection of radio waves from aircraft, and was able to suggest to the Tizard Committee a radio method, which not only provided early warning, but precise location as well. Moreover, he was able to support his proposals with calculations showing the practicability of his scheme. The committee were interested and encouraged Watson-Watt to set up a demonstration of the scattering of pulsed radio waves by aircraft in flight, and such was the enthusiasm and sense of purpose engendered by Sir Henry Tizard and his committee, that within about a month of the date of this meeting, a successful demonstration was carried out. This was on 26 February 1935. Once the Tizard Committee learnt of the successful demonstration, there was no hesitation on their part, and within a short time a new establishment was set up and a team of research scientists recruited. Watson-Watt had complete faith in his proposals and gladly left his work at the National Physical Laboratory to head the new team, and staked his reputation on the success of the venture with no more grounds than a few calculations and a sketchy experiment. It is of interest that from the earliest days of the new venture, Watson-Watt had no doubt that a vast new field in applied science had been opened. In fact matters moved very quickly once the backing of the Tizard Committee had been obtained. By June 1935 the 'sketchy experiment' had been replaced by a full-scale demonstration with aircraft followed out to 40 miles range, and large financial backing for this important defence measure was being provided by the Air Ministry and by the Treasury.

It is worth pausing a moment and reflecting that many

3

people could have invented radar, but the happy result in this case is a classic example of the results achievable by contact between those with a need and those with a technique which could meet this need. The contact here was between the Air Ministry seeking to improve British defences and Watson-Watt who was engaged on a technique without thought of a military application. This vital contact between the 'scientist' and the 'user' is necessary to get progress in almost any field of applied science. The difficulty is often security, but Britain was fortunate in having men like Wimperis and Tizard who saw clearly what was required, and were able to arrange the correct conditions to ensure that the problem of air defence was satisfactorily solved.

In case the reader at this stage is saying to himself that the idea of 'radar' is simple, the point should be made that without doing the detailed theoretical calculations, one would not really expect to be able to detect an aircraft at a range of 100 miles or so by monitoring the radio-frequency energy reflected back by the aircraft. The radar location of an aircraft involves transmitter powers of the order of $100 \text{ kW} = 10^5 \text{ W}$ with receivers sensitive to $10 \text{ m}\mu\mu\text{W} = 10^{-14} \text{ W}$, so that in the engineering sense, radar has an efficiency of only 10^{-19}. All the rest of the transmitter power is dissipated uselessly or lost in space.

Strangely enough at least two proposals for a radar system similar to the original Watson-Watt scheme were put forward by would-be inventors during the last war. One of these came from a schoolboy and like Watson-Watt he gave some theoretical calculations to indicate the probable range of performance obtainable. Because of the security then prevailing, these potential inventors could not be told that radar was already a reality, but efforts were made to direct them into suitable war work, where their scientific inventiveness could be usefully employed.

TYPES OF RADAR EQUIPMENT

The initial development of radar was to provide an early warning of the approach of enemy aircraft so that the fighter aircraft could be got off the ground in sufficient time to beat back the attacking force before they reached their objective. Fortunately timing of the invention of radar was right and by the outbreak of hostilities in 1939 Britain had in operation a substantial number of radar stations. These enabled the limited fighter aircraft resources to be in the right place at the right time during the Battle of Britain, and although the enemy had a huge attacking force of bomber aircraft, radar allowed the small fighter force to be conserved and their available strength directed where it was required. The result was that the attack was finally beaten back with disastrous losses to the enemy.

The main advantages of radar in these operations is that of denying the enemy the element of surprise. The Battle of Britain had been fought in the daytime and radar had provided a means of detecting aircraft at considerable distances from the island shores. However, the operation of radar is not affected by night or other adverse weather conditions, and so this provided Britain with a technical superiority in the Night Battle which followed. Night attacks were made by the enemy during moonlight nights, and by this time methods of ground control had been developed which allowed Royal Air Force Ground Controllers to give instructions by radio to the fighter pilots so that they could intercept the incoming enemy aircraft. This involved using radar to locate the position of the enemy aircraft and when the fighter aircraft had been directed into the immediate vicinity, using radar to determine progressively the relative positions of the fighter and enemy bomber aircraft and so complete the interception. For the final stages the fighter aircraft was able to make use of a radar equipment with forward-viewing facilities fitted in his own aircraft. This radar equipment, designated A.I. ('air interception') together with the ground stations G.C.I. ('ground control of interception stations'), helped the Royal Air Force to inflict very heavy losses on the enemy.

Radar also played an important part in the Battle of the Atlantic. Enemy submarines had the advantage initially. They were able to cruise at will at night and only needed to submerge and keep out of sight during the daytime. They were able to inflict large losses on shipping.

Radar was fitted to British aircraft patrolling the convoy routes. This was designated A.S.V. ('air to surface vessels', and was capable of detecting submarines.* There then followed a period during which the submarines were forced to remain submerged for long periods to preserve themselves from crippling attacks, and this so reduced their mobility that they

* It should be appreciated that radar is only able to locate a submarine if some part of it is above the water line.

were prevented from making effective attacks on allied shipping. The next action was with the enemy—they provided their submarines with receivers tuned to the transmitter frequency of the A.S.V. radars. This enabled them to listen in and obtain warning of the approach of radar-equipped aircraft. For a time the initiative was with the enemy and again shipping losses started to increase. The answer this time was to introduce an A.S.V. radar capable of operating on a much higher frequency (10,000 Mc/sec as compared with the 200 Mc/sec employed on the earlier equipments). This gave the advantage to the Allies until the Battle of the Atlantic was won. It may be noted at this stage that the higher frequency also allowed the range of detection on periscope targets* to be substantially increased as compared with that possible with the lower-frequency radar equipments.

Radar was also effective, particularly in the later stages of World War II, in overcoming the limitations of weather which threatened to cripple the size of our effort by providing aids to navigation, and providing new methods of target location, as well as blind bombing techniques. The most spectacular of the radar target location devices was named H_2S ('Home Sweet Home'), because it was also of value as a general navigational aid for getting the pilots 'back home' after completing their mission. H_2S was a microwave radar specifically designed for looking at ground echoes, and in conjunction with a special type of cathode-ray tube display, designated a P.P.I. ('plan position indicator'), it effectively provided a plan position indication of the countryside below the H_2S-equipped aircraft. As irregularities produced echoes according to their size, the built-up area of a city or factory site naturally produced a mass of echoes which could be clearly seen on the display. Moreover, the radar showed up clearly the position of coastlines, the routes of rivers, etc., and so was of the greatest value as a general navigational aid, which as it did not depend on the use of ground stations could be operated independently of the distance of the target from base.

In this short introduction we have not mentioned the use of radar by the Royal Navy or the Army, but sufficient has been said for the reader to realise that as the war proceeded, radar gradually changed its role from an aid to Britain's defences

---

* I.e. submerged submarines, but with a part of the periscope above the water line.

to being an auxiliary to her offensive programme. It may be noted here that, in general, the radar equipment may be land-, ship- or airborne, and the target reflecting the radiation may be a land feature (e.g. a cliff or a church spire), a ship, an aircraft,

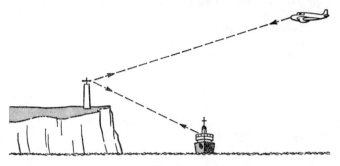

Fig. 2.

or a surfaced submarine; echoes are also received from the waves of the sea, and one of the major problems of radar is the detection of the wanted echo among unwanted echoes such as sea or land clutter.

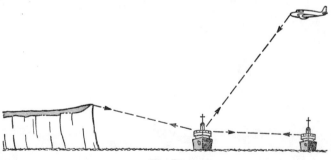

Fig. 3.

The applications of radar can perhaps be best understood in terms of echoes which are obtained when radar equipment is used in different locations. These applications are illustrated in Figs. 2, 3 and 4. In Fig. 2, for example, we have a ground radar equipment located on a cliff edge site. Echoes would therefore be received from aircraft passing within the range of detectiblity and thus the station provides an early warning function. It is possible that the same station could be used for accurate tracking of aircraft and perhaps therefore providing information for the ground control of interception of enemy aircraft, and perhaps also the control of anti-aircraft guns. Similarly, echoes would be received as shown from surface vessels sufficiently close to the station to be detected, and again if enemy craft are involved, the radar plots could be used for the control of fire from coastal batteries.

In Fig. 3 we illustrate the application of radar on board ship. Again echoes would be received from aircraft and surface vessels, providing the necessary information for air warning, sea search and fire control. Echoes would also be received from nearby coast-lines, a feature which is often of value in navigating in coastal waters. Echoes would also be obtained from icebergs if present in the sea, which again is a help in navigation.

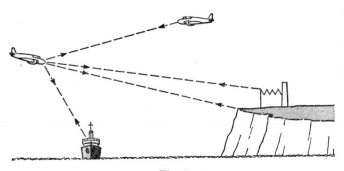

Fig. 4.

Finally, in Fig. 4, we illustrate the case of an aircraft equipped with radar. Echoes, in this case, would be received from other aircraft allowing air interceptions to be carried out at night, and if required air-to-air blind firing. Ships, or surfaced submarines would also give echoes enabling sea search and blind bombing attacks. In addition, coast-lines and hills would produce relatively large echoes which would be detectable at long range and aid navigation. Built-up areas would, as already explained, be recognised by the relatively large signals which are reflected back from them as compared with the corresponding signals from open country, and this aids navigation as well as providing information for blind bombing.

COMPONENTS OF A RADAR SET

The components of a simple radar set are shown in Fig. 5. The modulator produces a series of short d.c. pulses at the chosen recurrence frequency. These are converted into radar-frequency pulses in the transmitter and radiated into space by the transmitting aerial. At least a part of this energy leaks away across to the receiving aerial, is amplified by the receiver and produces a vertical deflection of the cathode-ray tube

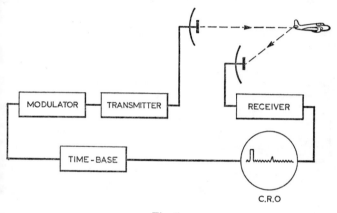

Fig. 5.

spot. This is the 'direct' or 'ground' pulse. The energy radiated by the transmitting aerial is radiated into space, and a very small fraction of it may be scattered back to the receiving aerial by any aircraft within range. This energy scattered back is amplified by the receiver and applied to produce a vertical deflection of the cathode-ray tube spot as before.

The trace of the cathode-ray tube moves across the screen from left to right once every cycle so that it appears to be stationary to the eye. The range of the aircraft is therefore determined by noting the position of the 'aircraft' echo along the time-base, noting that the ground pulse is, of course, at zero range.

As radar developed it was appreciated that duplex operation

9

was possible, namely, that a single aerial could be employed both for transmitting and receiving. It will be appreciated from reference to Fig. 5, and, of course, Fig. 1, that the aerial need only be connected to the transmitter during the period of operation of the transmitter pulse. After this short period of time it should be connected to the receiver, and if this switching can proceed in this way for every cycle one aerial can be employed for both transmitting and receiving. Suitable T.R. switches were designed during World War II and duplex operation of this sort was used on many of the later radar equipments. In many cases also the aerial system employed produced a narrow beam in the azimuthal plane. The display

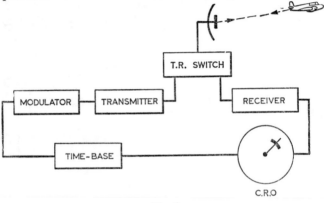

Fig. 6.

system was then of a special type known as the plan position indicator (P.P.I.). In this type of display the time-base is radial and starts from the centre of the tube. Instead of causing a deflection as in the type of presentation shown in Fig. 6, the presence of an echo causes the spot to brighten at the appropriate range. The aerial is arranged to rotate continuously and the time-base rotates in synchronism with it. It follows therefore that as the beam comes to a target, the spot brightens, traces a small arc of a circle and disappears again as the beam goes off target. In this way each echo within detectable range gives a small bright arc of a circle on the display at the appropriate range and azimuth. Furthermore, by using a cathode-ray tube with a long decay phosphor screen, with a decay period about equal to the period of rotation of the aerial, the presentation provides a plan position picture of all the aircraft within range of the station. Figure 6 shows the components of a typical radar set of this type, whilst Plate 1 shows the sort of presentation obtained. In some cases, e.g. fixed installations, it is an advantage to draw on the face of the cathode-ray tube the principal features of the countryside surrounding the station.

The early radar equipments in Britain (C.H.—'chain home') were designed to detect aircraft approaching our coasts and used wavelengths in the 6–15 m band. They required large expensive towers, the transmitting towers being generally 360 ft high and receiving towers 240 ft. These towers were necessary to obtain satisfactory radiation intensity at elevations below 10°, aerials some 10 wavelengths above the ground being essential for this purpose. A peak power of 200 kW was employed, a pulse being transmitted every 1/25 sec, and ranges of the order of 140 miles were obtained on aircraft flying at 15,000 ft. A workable system on these lines was available at the outbreak of World War II, and the chain of stations was rapidly extended round the south and east coasts, and less rapidly round the west and north. Minor improvements were made later, and some stations were equipped with 1 MW transmitters, but fundamentally the system remained unchanged throughout the war from the type existing in 1939.

The main line of development lay at shorter wavelengths, e.g. the gun-laying equipments (G.L.) on the 3 m band (the use of shorter wavelengths allowing the increased precision necessary), the coastal chain (C.H.L.—'chain home low') for the detection of low-flying aircraft (the increased height of the aerial in terms of wavelengths allowing increased ranges of detection at low angles of elevation) and the ground control of interception stations (G.C.I.) both on 1·5 m wavelength, early airborne 1·5 m equipment and the very great developments in all fields on wavelengths of 10 cm and below which became general in 1942. Naval developments showed the same tendency and towards the end of the war centimetre wave equipments became predominant for all functions. Magnetrons*

* A magnetron is an electron tube characterised by the interaction of electrons with the electric field of a circuit element in crossed steady electric and magnetic fields to produce a.c. power output.

were developed to give output powers of the order of 200 kW at a wavelength of 10 cm for airborne applications (e.g. A.I., A.S.V. and H_2S) and 1 MW 10 cm magnetrons were later produced for ground applications, where a greater bulk and weight of equipment was allowable. Ranges of 8–10 miles became possible on aircraft targets with A.I. equipments, as well as reasonable ranges with high resolution ground radar equipments, although the longer wavelengths still retained their usefulness for certain special applications.

The reasons for the downward trend of wavelengths will become clear from the later chapters of this book, but it should be emphasised at the outset that the techniques which made these achievements possible were sometimes new and highly original and sometimes an extension of those common in radio practice. The lowering to 1·5 m and even to 50 cm was a normal type of development following more or less conventional lines, using, for example, triode oscillators in the transmitters and pentode radio-frequency amplifiers in the receivers, whereas the whole of the work at 10 cm and below was very much in the category of highly original and fundamental work and stands out as the most brilliant single invention since radar itself. It will be appreciated that the downward trend in wavelengths was in some cases necessary as a counter-measure (e.g. to combat radio listening in the Battle of the Atlantic). In other cases to improve radar cover at low elevations, and in still other cases to improve the precision of radar location. In all these cases the move to microwavelengths was a tremendous step which placed the enemy at a grave disadvantage.

APPLICATIONS SINCE WORLD WAR II

During the war the applications of radar were predominantly of a military character, but since this time many civil applications have been found. It is probably natural that the use of radar as an aid to civil aviation and marine navigation should follow quickly after the cessation of hostilities and this was the case. It has also found application in connection with the control of traffic at airfields, the study of meteorology, assistance in weather forecasting, and not least its use for storm warning. Ornithologists have been able to make more detailed studies of the migration habits of birds, particularly along the sea coasts—using radar. Another major field of application is in connection with surveying, particularly of undeveloped, or inaccessible terrain.

Radar has also found appliction in probing the planets. In 1946, for example, the Signal Corps scientists at Fort Monmouth were the first to bounce radar signals off the moon. A few years later even this achievement seemed small with the successful radar probing of segments of the moon's surface and even of distant planets.

Radar techniques have also played a significant part in many new sciences, e.g. radio spectrometry, radio astronomy, tracking of earth satellites and space probes, etc. These and other matters are discussed in detail in the later chapters.

Plate 2 illustrates some of the many applications of radar.

CHAPTER TWO

GROUND RADAR SYSTEMS DURING WORLD WAR II

C.H. RADARS

As explained in the introductory chapter, work on the early warning radars began in Britain in 1936 with the setting up of five stations, about 25 miles apart, to protect London and the Thames estuary, and by the time war broke out in 1939* this chain had been extended to cover the greater part of the south and east coasts of England and Scotland. It was improved and extended during the actual war, and new equipments were provided, particularly in the later stages of the war, but C.H. remained the basis of the British Reporting System for the greater part of this time.

The main chain operated on frequencies between 22 and 28 Mc/sec, the choice being decided from a consideration of the range performance obtainable using available or easily produced transmitting tubes and receiving valves and current radio techniques. For my more knowledgeable readers it may be noted that these stations operated on a wavelength in excess of the critical wavelength for piercing the E-layer of the ionosphere at oblique incidence and consequently, under suitable conditions, strong reflections could occur due to waves which travel to and from the radar station via the upper atmosphere. These reflections are from considerable ranges, and so it is necessary to employ a very low repetition frequency to ensure that they cause no interference with the tracking of aircraft at the shorter ranges. The pulse repetition frequency chosen was 25 cycles/sec, giving the time between consecutive traces as 40 millisec. In order to track aircraft up to a maximum range of 200 miles, it is necessary to arrange that the cathode-ray tube completes its journey across the face of the tube in about 2 millisec,† and is blacked out for 38 millisec before the next time-base starts. The 'scatter', as it is usually called, originates from points on the earth's surface at ranges between

* Much of this story is given in Watson-Watt's book *Three Steps to Victory* (Odhams, 1957).

† This follows from delay is 10·7 μsec per mile.

2000 and 4000 miles, and so it arrives during the black-out period and is not seen on the following trace. However, under phenomenal conditions scatter is returned from ranges in excess of this, and are therefore seen on the following trace. If this occurs it naturally interferes with the tracking of real targets, and facilities were therefore provided for reducing the pulse repetition frequency to 12·5 cycles/sec when necessary.

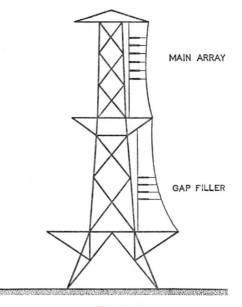

MAIN ARRAY

GAP FILLER

Fig. 7.

Separate antennas were used for transmitting and receiving. The transmitting antenna was an array of 6 half-wave aerials spaced vertically* as shown in Fig. 7 with suitable tuned reflectors and floodlights a quadrant of a sphere in front of the station as shown in Fig. 8, the greater part of the energy

* The vertical stacking has the effect of increasing the vertical directivity of the transmissions. However, reflections off the ground have the effect of interfering with the propagation at certain angles of elevation, producing reinforcement at certain angles and interference (i.e. cancellation) at other angles.

being confined within 20° of the horizontal and within approximately ± 50° of the line of shoot.

Apart from the free-space directivity of the antenna in the vertical plane which is influenced as already mentioned by the vertical aperture of the array, i.e. the number of elements in the vertical stacking, it should be appreciated that the radiation arriving at an illuminated target comes by two paths, first direct and then after reflection from the ground. The polar diagram in the vertical plane will differ from that for free space since the radiations arriving by the two paths may interfere with each other. In general, the radiation pattern in the vertical plane comprises a series of maxima and minima,

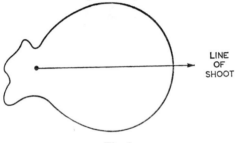

LINE
OF
SHOOT

Fig. 8.

where the radiation travelling via the two paths arrive in phase and reinforce each other, or arrive out of phase and cancel each other. Figure 9 shows the vertical polar diagram of the C.H. transmitting array. Gaps in the coverage due to ground effects of the sort described above can be seen at $4\frac{1}{2}$°, 9°, etc. In practice, it is usual to provide a second transmitting aerial, designated the gap-filling array, which is at a lower height and which therefore produces an interference pattern with maxima and minima at different angles of elevation to the main array. This is shown by the dotted curve in Fig. 9.

The essential details of the receiving system are shown in Fig. 10. Signals are received in two crossed dipoles and are compared in a goniometer to determine the azimuth of the re-radiating aircraft. With this type of apparatus an aircraft on a reciprocal bearing would give exactly the same setting of the goniometer. This type of ambiguity was avoided on the C.H. stations by having switchable reflectors behind the

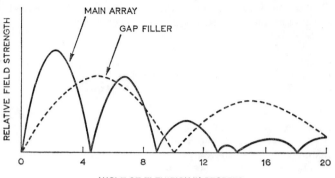

Fig. 9.

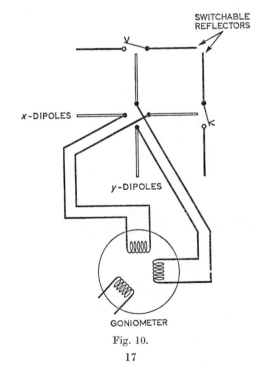

Fig. 10.

17

dipoles (see Fig. 10), and noting the effect on the received signal of switching a reflector in and out of circuit.

Height-finding was performed by making use of the lobe pattern of the receiving aerials (two were again used at different heights). This is probably best understood by plotting the relative signal strengths from the C.H. height-finding aerials. It will be noted that the ratio of the two signal strengths varies according to the angle of elevation. This is shown in Fig. 11. Hence by measuring the ratio of the two signal strengths, the angle of elevation can be deduced, or by feeding in the range as well, the flying height of the aircraft can be deduced. In fact, the output from the two receiving aerials can be fed to the x-y-coils of the goniometer used for d.f. measurements and the setting of the goniometer for zero current is related to the ratio of the two currents and therefore to the angle of elevation.

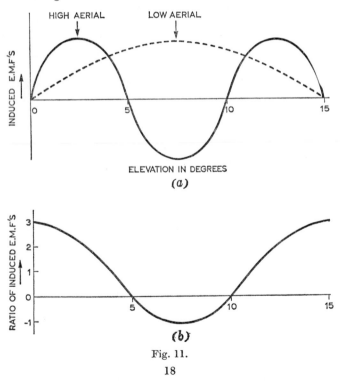

Fig. 11.

18

It will be noted by reference to Fig. 11 that there can be some ambiguity if aircraft are first observed only at high angles of elevation, although these can often be quickly resolved by noting the results of a series of readings. In fact, in almost all cases aircraft are first observed at relatively long range and at low angles of elevation, and so this difficulty does not arise. In the C.H. stations used during the war a small computer was effectively used (using electromagnetic relays and telephone uniselectors instead of the transistors, which are used in modern computers), in which were fed in the measured range of the target, the goniometer setting using the d.f. aerials and the goniometer setting using the elevation aerials. This was very convenient, because apart from carrying out the necessary arithmetical operations to determine the azimuth and height of the aircraft, the machine could make allowance for the various corrections for site imperfections, calibrations, etc.

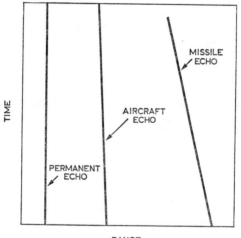

Fig. 12.

The display system was the usual type of A-scope (see Appendix 2 and Chapter One) in which the echo signals appear as vertical deflections on a horizontal time-base. As designed it had some obvious shortcomings, namely, the need for large and expensive towers, gaps in the vertical coverage (decided by site imperfections), and coverage on low-flying aircraft was poor. It also had a real limitation in its handling capacity, but in spite of these shortcomings, operators including females belonging to the W.R.A.F.S. quickly became very expert in using it to maximum advantage and it played a most important part in the mass-enemy raids on the country during the Battle of Britain, and, as has been said many times: 'without the C.H. radars this country might very well have been defeated'.

It is interesting that towards the end of the war when the enemy began to use V-2 rockets for bombarding London, that the C.H. radars again played a vital part. The V-2 rockets were cylindrical, roughly about 30 ft in length and 5 ft in diameter and carried a war-head of about 1 ton of high explosive. The problem was to detect these rockets soon after they had left their firing points so that some early warning could be provided, and so that the exact locations of the firing points could be deduced for later 'pin-point' bombing operations. Microwave radar could be used for this purpose, but because most of the reflection from such targets is specular,* the signal strength obtained with microwave radar after reflection at the target was very small and detection probabilities except under conditions of very favourable aspect were poor. With the C.H. radars, on the other hand, the rocket behaved roughly as $\lambda/2$ dipole and a very strong response resulted providing detection ranges of the order of 100 miles.

Another problem was that of identification of the V-2 response. The method adopted was to take advantage of the very high velocity of the projectile. An intensity-modulation type of display was employed as shown in Fig. 12. Here the time-base with echoes appearing as brightness modulation on the time-trace was caused to move vertically and trace out a range-time roster. On such a display permanent echoes (corresponding to fixed reflecting objects) appear as vertical lines; aircraft echoes (because of the relatively modest speeds of aircraft) appear as lines whose departure from the vertical is

* This is reflection in which a beam of radio waves appears, after reflection, to proceed from an image of the source in the reflecting surface. This is also used in connection with the reflection of light, and the reader who has studied elementary optics may remember that for such reflection the angle of incidence equals the angle of reflection. This, of course, is in contrast to 'diffuse reflection' or scattering, when the reflected rays come off at many angles from the reflecting surface. A smooth regular surface such as a cylindrical rocket gives mostly specular reflection and very little scattering.

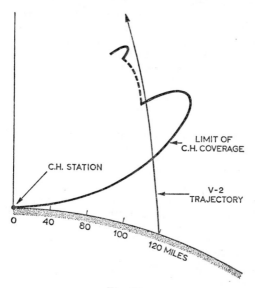

Fig. 13.

slight, whereas V-2 echoes (because of the much higher speeds*
involved) appear as lines with very much greater departure
from the vertical. Furthermore, the rockets used trajectories
which carried them above the coverage of the normal radar
stations, and so, in practice, observations could only be made
with the conventional stations on the early part of the trajectory (see Fig. 13). This, however, was an advantage rather
than a disadvantage, as the observations on the initial part
of the trajectory (which was almost vertical) allowed the track
to be reproduced backwards to determine the firing point, and
this could be done with great accuracy.

It will be appreciated that the observation time did not
allow a d.f. to be accomplished, and even if it had, such a d.f.
would not have been of sufficient accuracy for the purpose in
view. Instead, it was decided to rely on observations from two

* It should be noted that it is the radial velocity which is important, but by observing at several radar sites, it will be clear that if
a particular rocket has no radial velocity when viewed from one
site it will have appreciable radial velocity from another.

21

or more stations and use range cuts from these two or more stations to determine the location of the firing point. Range can, of course, be measured extremely accurately with the C.H. stations and so this method proved extremely accurate. The outcome of this battle will be known to all but the youngest of my readers. The attack on London with V-2 rockets was a very bad experience, but fortunately it did not last long. The early warning system worked well and undoubtedly saved many lives, but more important, radar provided good information regarding the firing points used, and before very long the Royal Air Force with the firing-point information was able to put them out of action by accurate bombing.

C.H.L. AND C.D. RADARS

The limitations of the C.H. radars were known before they were built, and a special chain of radars were designed and built to supplement the C.H. and provide good cover against low-flying aircraft. These operated on a frequency of 200 Mc/sec or a wavelength of 1·5 m, and by siting them as far as possible on cliff-edge sites they were able to illuminate and view low-flying aircraft. Initially they were used also against ship targets, for which, in general, precise d.f. information was required. In such cases, the 'split-beam' or

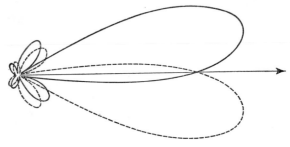

Fig. 14.

beam-switching technique was employed. In this an array is used which can send out either of two beams displaced slightly in azimuth. The beams are sent out in rapid succession, and the display system is arranged to show the relative received amplitudes. When the amplitude received from the two beams is the same, it is known that the bearing of the target is exactly half-way between the two axes as shown in Fig. 14.

22

This method gives a much greater accuracy than the single-beam type of equipment, because firstly, we are operating on the steep sides of the polar diagram instead of a maximum where the rate of change of signal strength with angle is small, and secondly, the display system can be arranged to show the sign of the signal inequality and indicates therefore which way the aerial has to be moved to obtain an exact balance.

The C.H.L. array consisted of horizontally polarised dipoles

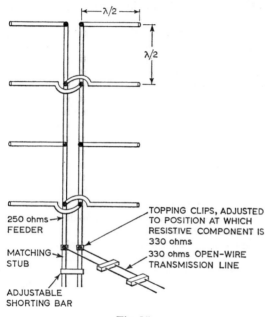

Fig. 15.

arranged broadside in front of a wire-netting reflector. The array consisted of four bays side by side, $5\lambda/4$ apart, each consisting of a stack of four centre-fed full-wave radiators $\lambda/2$ apart as shown in Fig. 15. The method of feeding power to such an array is also illustrated in the diagram. It is achieved by what is called stub-matching. The problem is to match the impedance of the feeder line to the aerial, and this is achieved by short-circuiting the stub at a convenient point and choosing a point along the stub for the connection of the feeder line so that the line impedance just equals the impedance presented by the aerial via the interconnecting stub, and therefore provides a 'match'.

As mentioned earlier the C.H.L. system was the first to employ a single aerial for both transmission and reception by means of spark-gap switching. This was of particular value when the C.H.L. system was used to provide, what is in effect, a radio searchlight. As the beam sweeps round it 'illuminates' a sector of the sky; any aircraft in that sector scatters radiation back to the station and is detected.

With the introduction of continuously rotating beam systems came a new form of display—the plan position indicator or P.P.I. This takes the form of a rotating radial time-base display, the direction of rotation being at all times parallel to the direction of the aerial beam. The received pulses are displayed as brightness modulation of the cathode-ray tube spot, and so aircraft responses produce on this presentation a short arc of brightness in a position relative to the centre of the tube which corresponds directly to the distance and direction of the target from the aerial system. In the case of the C.H.L. and certain other types of radar stations it is convenient to track the aircraft directly on a map drawn on the face of the C.R.O. Although it is not capable of the highest accuracy of azimuth determination, the plan position indicator has been widely adopted (and is still used) for radar installations on account of the continuous presentation which it offers of plotting a large number of echoes without losing the general picture.

At a later stage in World War II, the C.H.L. stations with continuous rotating aerials and P.P.I. were employed exclusively for tracking low-flying aircraft and providing information about the general situation, and special stations, designated C.D. ('Coastal Defence') stations, with facilities for 'split-beam' d.f. were provided for accurate tracking of ships and fire-control purposes.

It may be noted that where the highest accuracy is of secondary importance, it is usual to read the range of the target directly from the cathode-ray tube (type A display). In other cases a range knob is employed, which is linked with a mechanical cursor whose position is adjusted to correspond with the leading edge of the target echo. A magnified display (obtained by speeding up the time-base for a part of the scan bracketing the target echo) allows the setting to be made with fair accuracy, although reference must be made to the calibration scale and, in general, interpolation between the calibration pips. A more satisfactory method which has been employed on certain long-range gunnery sets, and is a real advantage when the highest precision is required, is to use two traces, on one of which the echo signals are displayed, the other being a calibration scale. A small portion of the signal trace (corresponding to the distance between two calibration pips, say to 1000 yards) is speeded up, and since the calibration trace is developed by the same circuits, this also has a speeded-up portion corresponding to the same limits. Up to this point, therefore, the accuracy of the range determination depends on the scale of the picture as in the previous methods. However, the range wheel which controls the position of the expanded portion of the trace is geared to a continuously adjustable phase shifter in the output of the crystal-controlled oscillator from which the calibration pips are derived. One complete rotation of the phase shifter corresponds to a change of phase of 2π, or one complete period of the crystal-controlled oscillator. Therefore, if one of the calibration pips is set opposite the ground wave and the hand wheel is rotated until this pip is set opposite the selected echo, the number of rotations of the hand wheel gives an accurate measure of the range of the target. Thus, if the crystal-controlled oscillator produces 1000 yard pips, and if it is necessary to rotate the hand wheel through 12 complete revolutions and 0·65 of a complete rotation, the range of the target is evidently 12,650 yards.

G.C.I. RADARS

During daylight, radar inaccuracies of a mile or two, height errors of a few thousand feet, or delays of a minute or two in passing information through a filter room and through a Sector H.Q. to the day-fighter squadrons were not serious. Provided that the fighters could be directed with sufficient accuracy actually to see their bomber targets their superior speed did the rest. However, the possibility of night attacks with bomber forces was clearly a different problem, and fortunately by the time the enemy switched his forces to night attacks we had an interception technique worked out. The state of preparedness for the night attacks was achieved by concentrating a great deal of work into a remarkably few weeks of really intense study, design work, manufacturing effort, and we were fortunate in having six ground controlled interception stations (G.C.I. as they came to be known), completed and crews in training by the time the night attack really started. We also had a number of squadrons of A.I. ('air interception') equipped aircraft with trained crews.

Dealing with the ground equipment first, it was realised early that to avoid the time delays and to ensure that up-to-date information was used to control the interceptions the ground controllers would have to operate from the radar stations themselves. Up till this time and during the very successful day battles the controllers had operated from their Sector H.Q. Second, it was appreciated that the plan position indicator used with a rotating aerial system would allow the controller to observe the positions of both the enemy bomber and the fighter aircraft being used for the interception, and therefore this system also allowed him to observe their *relative* positions, and determine the direction in which the fighter aircraft should fly to effect an interception. We therefore knew that the equipment should be based on the C.H.L. station with a P.P.I., but should be designed to give gap-free cover in the vertical plane from angles of elevation of 4° to 40° and with a maximum range of about 70 miles. The method used was to employ the C.H.L. broadside array, but sited on a flat site with the centre of the aerial about 2λ above the ground. Initially the C.H.L. array was divided in two halves so as to form two arrays each of four bays and each bay comprising a stack consisting of two centre-fed full-wave radiators, one being effectively at a mean height of $7\frac{1}{2}$ ft and other at a mean height of $12\frac{1}{2}$ ft, and use these as a main aerial and a gap-filler. Later, however, it was realised that a better result could be achieved by feeding the two halves in-phase as the main aerial, and then as a gap-filler use the two aerials in anti-phase.* The vertical polar diagram of the complete aerial when used for transmitting in this way is shown in Fig. 16.

Elevation was determined by an adaptation of the spaced aerial technique as previously employed on the C.H. radars. This is, of course, a simple matter if it is possible to align the aerial beam in the direction of the target aircraft and maintain this setting during the time that the goniometer (or its equivalent) is adjusted for zero reading. For purposes of G.C.I., however, interruption of the plan position display is unacceptable, and a method is obviously needed which allows

---

* This involved switching in an extra $\lambda/2$ of transmission line in the line feeding one of the arrays.

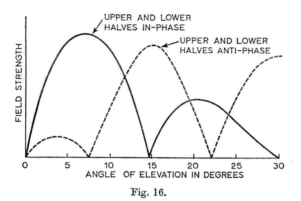

Fig. 16.

elevation-finding with a continuous rotating aerial. A number of suggestions were put forward, but the most successful, and the one which was widely adopted for G.C.I., uses two receiving aerials at different heights (i.e. $7\frac{1}{2}$ ft and $12\frac{1}{2}$ ft)* above the ground. The two received signals are presented side by side

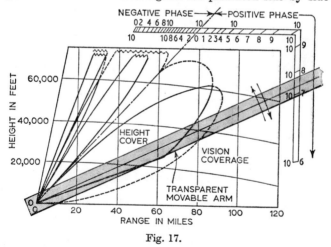

Fig. 17.

* It will be appreciated that these aerial heights had to be used in any case when common aerial working was adopted, since these heights are required when the aerial is operating in the transmitting mode.

27

as deflections on a C.R.O. in a similar way to that already described for 'beam switching', an electronic switch being employed to connect the two aerials to the receiver in rapid succession, just as in azimuth determination. A long afterglow C.R.O. is employed to 'hold' the transient signals, and although the time the target is 'in beam' is short, the signals are retained in afterglow sufficiently long to enable an experienced operator to estimate the ratio of the two signal amplitudes. This estima-

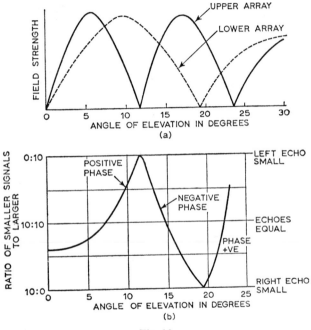

Fig. 18.

tion was done by eye, no mechanical or optical aid being employed. This may be thought to be rather surprising, but during the war R.A.F. operators who were familiar with interpolating in tenths of a grid square on plotting maps, found they were able to estimate the ratio with an accuracy better than 5% of the larger signal. This was sufficiently good, since the practice was to take several ratios on successive rotations of the aerial and to plot the results on a height conversion board (see Fig. 17) and obtain an average value for the height of the target.

For the simple type of G.C.I. set with aerials at $7\frac{1}{2}$ and $12\frac{1}{2}$ ft, the vertical polar diagrams for the two arrays are shown in Fig. 18(a) and the ratio of the signals from the two arrays as a function of the angle of elevation is shown in Fig. 18(b). It will be noted that although the system is insensitive to changes in elevation below about 4°, it allows satisfactory elevation-finding between 4° and 21° providing positive and negative phases can be distinguished. This latter facility is, in fact, already available because if we determine whether the target is seen more clearly with the transmitter feeding the two aerials in-phase or anti-phase, we obtain the 'phase check' desired for resolving the height-finding ambiguities.*

The time scale set for the supply of the G.C.I. equipments was met. On 16 October 1940 the first of twelve G.C.I. sets was completed at T.R.E. and by 18 October it had been installed at the selected site and was used in operations. Such was the pace of activity in those hectic days! By Christmas Day, six of the new ground installations were complete and the last of the twelve was ready on 6 January 1941. A similar intensive effort was made to produce sufficient A.I. sets to equip first Blenheim and then Beaufighter aircraft.

The night fighters were not immediately successful, and looking back it is apparent that a large part of our difficulties when the night attack did start was in getting the R.A.F. (ground and air crews) trained to use the new devices to best advantage. However, enemy losses increased month by month until, in May 1941, 102 enemy night bombers were shot down in the month's operation by our night fighters and 172 were assessed as probably destroyed or damaged. During the critical five months the casualty rate suffered by night bombers attacking this country rose from less than $\frac{1}{2}$% to over 7% and the result was that enemy attacks substantially ceased—we had won the 'Night Battle'. The historians tell us that this second important victory in which radar played a significant part was achieved with the aid of a few G.C.I. sets and perhaps not more than 100 A.I. sets.

This type of G.C.I. equipment was used a great deal both at home and abroad and although a number of different

* If the signal increases in magnitude when the transmitter array is fed in anti-phase, the angle of elevation must be between 12° and 19°, i.e. negative phase.

versions were produced, basically they were all the same. However, with the coming of microwaves, special height-finding equipments were installed as auxiliaries at the more important G.C.I. sites. The use of a very narrow beam, controllable in elevation to determine height, renders the performance of the radar free from dependence on the surrounding terrain except only for the very low elevation for which appreciable energy is reflected off the ground. The height-finding accuracy is therefore mainly dependent on controllable factors such as beamwidth, the overall mechanical accuracy and the method of display.

The first V.E.B. system to be designed operated on a wavelength of 1·5 m. The aerial consisted of 56 full-wave elements in a vertical stack, and elevation finding was carried out by locating the direction of maximum response as the beam tilted up and down. The movement of the beam was achieved electrically by varying the relative phases of groups of dipoles. This type of V.E.B. operating on 1·5 m demanded a large and expensive tower as will be seen from Plate 3, and with the advent of microwaves a centimetric type of V.E.B. was proposed and has since been used on a large scale.

The centimetric V.E.B. consists of a cylindrical parabolic reflector fed by means of a slotted waveguide.* One of the early systems is shown in Plate 4. The vertical aperture is often quite large. In one service equipment, it is of the order of 60λ giving a beamwidth of about 1½°. Motion of the beam is provided by mechanical or electrical means, the favourite electrical method being motion of a dielectric section in the guide which varies the relative phases of the primary radiators, i.e. the slots in the waveguide, and hence swings the beam in elevation.

The beam has, of course, to be set in azimuth from the indications of the associated search radar equipment (i.e. the P.P.I.) and can only view the aircraft in height in this sector. It is therefore necessary in certain circumstances to employ more than one height-finder, and this is certainly the case in the post-war developments. It should be noted, however, that a range marker can be used on the P.P.I. to mark a particular target, and the circuits producing the brightness modulation

* A slot in a conducting surface can behave as a radiating element. In the case of the centimetric V.E.B. a waveguide carrying radio-frequency power is used in which are cut a number of slots. The system therefore behaves as a line of simple dipoles.

for the strobe marker on the P.P.I. can be used to produce a strobe to mark the required echo in range on the elevation display.

To obtain the highest accuracy in elevation finding the beam-switching technique may be employed. This is similar to the beam-switching technique used for accurate azimuth determination and allows an accuracy of a few minutes of arc. It has been used on most of the radars for fire-control purposes.

For most other purposes it is convenient to scan the beam in elevation continuously and then a special display is necessary. The most common is the range-elevation scan with brightness

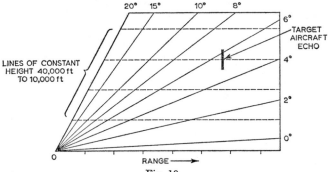

Fig. 19.

modulation. With this, lines of constant height are hyperbolae. A more realistic display is obtained by arranging that the co-ordinates of the display are $r\alpha$ and r (where r is the range and α is the elevation). Lines of constant height are now approximately straight as shown in Fig. 19.

The V.E.B. method of elevation finding gives a satisfactory performance only when the elevation is greater than half the vertical beamwidth. With the 60λ aperture equipment already referred to this means for elevations greater than about $\frac{3}{4}°$.

FIGHTER DIRECTION STATIONS

We have so far considered radar equipments involving scanning in *one* dimension in azimuth, or in elevation. In some cases scanning in two dimensions, in elevation as well as azimuth was a requirement. An example of the type of station was met in designing the so-called fighter direction stations. These stations were originally built to enable ground controllers to direct fighter sweeps over enemy territory and were later used with much success for general navigational purposes. They operated on a frequency band 500–600 Mc/sec* and used an aerial system consisting of a single dipole element at the focus of a wire-mesh paraboloidal reflector 30 ft in diameter with the axis of the latter at 5° to the horizontal. Arrangements were required for rotating this structure round a vertical axis at about 12° per sec and, simultaneously the dipole was required to execute a simple-harmonic motion in the aperture plane of the paraboloid with a semi-amplitude of 11 in. and a frequency of 12–15 cycles/sec. This movement caused the radar beam to scan rapidly from 0° to 10° in elevation while the whole system rotated slowly over any desired sector in azimuth. The relatively high frequency of movement of the dipole arm was necessary in order to scan the solid angle corresponding to $\pm$ 60° in azimuth and $\pm$ in 10° in elevation at least twice and preferably three times per minute, as a slower rate of scan would have meant a very discontinuous view of the aerial activity, and this was operationally unacceptable. The aerial is shown in Plate 5.

A small number of stations of this type were erected on the south coast to detect and locate enemy aircraft movements anywhere between Skagerrak and the Bay of Biscay and between Calais and Cologne. These mid-war fighter sweeps were very successful, although they could not, by their very nature, make such dramatic news as did the big-scale clashes of the Battle of Britain and the Bomber Offensive.

The technique was to watch for enemy aircraft movements and when suitable formations were seen to be collecting, send in fighter sweeps from this country to attack the enemy in enemy-occupied country, usually arranging for our fighter sweeps flying very fast to attack from above, and inflict losses not only on enemy aircraft in the air but also aircraft on the ground. It will be appreciated that the fighter direction stations were uniquely able to provide the appropriate information to enable these operations to take place. First, both long-range information up to 250 miles was provided in both plan position and elevation, and moreover the display could be selective to 'see', say, the high-flying aircraft on the P.P.I. and 'black out' those at lower elevations, or to "see" the lower fliers and 'black out' those at higher elevations. This is, of

* The operating frequency could be varied as an anti-jamming measure.

course, a technique which has been used after the war with high-frequency equipments on an even more ambitious scale.

Another interesting method of height-finding associated more with the Americans than the British is the so-called V-beam system. Two transmitters and two aerials are used. The first aerial produces a narrow beam in azimuth and a wide coverage in elevation. The second produces a similar beam, but in a plane inclined at 45° to the vertical, the planes of the two beams intersecting in a horizontal line. The two aerials (and this line) rotate together at a uniform speed of about 6 r.p.m. in such a way that the vertical beam comes first. It will be quite clear that a very low target would be seen at the intersection of the two beams and would appear as a single echo. A high aircraft, however, would be seen on the vertical beam first, and there would be a delay of a fraction of a revolution before the target appears in the 45° beam. By making a suitable display of the indications which appear in the two beams it is possible, very simply, to determine the height of any aircraft. Since the rotation is continuous, height can be found continuously in much the same manner as the plan position information is supplied. A few stations of this type were used towards the end of the last war and these operated on a wavelength of 10 cm, but although they gave good information, they were somewhat limited in range and never approached the maximum range of the lower frequency early warning radars. As will be seen by reference to Chapter Ten, modern radars have tended to use different techniques.

EMPLOYMENT OF RADAR DATA

It will be appreciated that the presentation of the echo signals on a C.R.O. by no means completes the problem of designing an operationally useful radar system. It is necessary that some action is taken on the basis of this information, and this calls for some organisation. In some cases, e.g. in fire control problems, this information can be fed into a predictor to compute automatically the future positions of targets and this predictor can be used for controlling the orientation of the guns.

In the early days of the war the radar plots from the various C.H. stations were transmitted to Fighter Command H.Q. by land lines. Because of the shortcomings of the early radar equipments and the 'blind spots' in the coverage of individual stations, it was essential to combine the information from all the radar stations at a central point. This was done at a so-called 'filter station'. As the plots were received over the telephone a plotter placed coloured disk markers on the grid positions indicated. Very often two or more stations were simultaneously plotting the same target, so that several girls might be putting down counters presenting the same information. Special officers, known as 'filterers', stood by the girls at the large plotting board and decided, for example, if two adjacent tracks were really separate, or represented the same aircraft. After examination the filterer would put on the board a small plaque that gave his best estimate of the identity, position, speed, height and number of aircraft in the formation. The whole process was observed by further officers, usually on a balcony overlooking the plotting board. These officers had information regarding the plans of our own aircraft movements, availability of fighter aircraft, etc., and they decided which formations should be plotted by each station. This was the method used in the day attacks by the enemy—the so-called 'Battle of Britain', and as we have seen, the method was a great success. However, with the coming of night attacks, it was appreciated that the control would have to move from Fighter Command H.Q. to the individual G.C.I. stations, although the Filter Rooms were still required for providing an appreciation of the general situation.

The design of the presentation equipment for G.C.I. and fighter direction stations involved, of course, many subsidiary equipments. Thus, large-scale plan position indicators were considered. These were of two main types, namely, projection type in which an optical image of the C.R.O. screen was projected on to a large screen giving a much magnified picture, and the use of the so-called skiatron* display which also allowed a flat, large-scale display.

In some cases an attempt was made to provide a three-dimensional display so that height could be presented on the same picture displaying the plan position picture.

INTERFERENCE

At various stages during the last war the enemy interfered

* This is a type of C.R.O. in which the screen, coated with an alkali halide, momentarily darkens under the action of an electron beam. These tubes are normally used in projection systems.

with our (the allies') radar equipment by putting out signals on the wavelengths we were using and so produced a lot of 'clutter' on the time-bases of our C.R.O. displays and so prevented these equipments from being used effectively. Various palliatives were introduced to minimise the effect of this jamming, but the most effective was, of course, to change the wavelength used. Thus there was a war of wavelengths and by multiplying the wavelengths used the enemy was forced to put in a very large effort to achieve any result. Furthermore, by retaining a few special wavelengths for important operations, the element of surprise could always be trusted to give us an advantage, at least, for a time.

In some cases, of course, we wanted to jam their equipments. This was necessary, for example, when we sent our bombers over enemy territory and there was the possibility of enemy radar tracking these aircraft with a view to taking retaliatory action, either by ground artillery or by fighter aircraft. In some cases it was also necessary to spoof the enemy regarding the nature and the size of our attacks. The most spectacular of these operations was on the D-day landings. Allied forces had been careful to put the majority of the enemy coastal warning radars out of action by sustained bombings before D-day, but apparently by mistake (or so the enemy were to believe) one radar was left operating. On D-day one small ship was sent in radar view of this station, but it was equipped with most elaborate radio equipment so that it produced a great multitude of echoes on the enemy radar's C.R.O. and gave the impression that a great operation was taking place. In fact the real operation took place at another location and the spoof radar signals engaged the attention of the enemy for some hours and prevented concentration of resisting troops at the right location to engage the landing forces for a vital period of time.

Another method which was used with some success, particularly against the higher frequency equipments, was by the use of thin strips of metal foil. These were cut to the correct length so that each piece resonated as a dipole to enemy radio-frequency. When this material, which went under the code word 'Window', was dispensed from aircraft large volumes of space could be filled with it. It fell at a speed of only a few miles per hour and the strong signals it returned so effectively masked the radar signals from aircraft that accurate location of our aircraft by the enemy was prevented.

CHAPTER THREE

AIRBORNE RADAR

INTRODUCTION

The first radar produced in Britain weighed many tons, and it is not to be wondered at therefore, that the feat of compression and simplification to produce an equipment suitable for installation in an aircraft took an appreciable time. In the early days when the work was carried out on a wavelength of 7 m, the transmitter was used on the ground and only the radar receiver was carried in the aircraft. These experiments were abortive and by September 1939 a primitive form of A.S.V. ('air to surface vessels'), A.S.V. Mk. I, operating on 200 Mc/sec had been evolved, and an improved equipment A.S.V. Mk. II was installed in Coastal Command aircraft in September 1940. The first sinking of an enemy U-boat with their use occurred in February 1941.

In this chapter some details will be given of the development of the major airborne radar equipments, A.S.V. ('air to surface vessels'), A.I. ('air interception') and H₂S ('Home Sweet Home'), and their roles in the 'Battle of the Atlantic', the 'Night Battle' and the 'Bombing Offensive'.

BATTLE OF THE ATLANTIC

The sinking of the *Athenia* by an enemy U-boat on the first evening of the war was a shocking beginning to the U-boat activity, and appeared to many to herald worse events for the future. However, the U-boat menace did not really begin to build up until they began to operate from the newly acquired bases in the French ports of the Bay of Biscay. U-boats crossed the bay in their passage to and from the shipping lanes and it was usual to travel submerged by day to avoid visual detection, and surface at night to recharge the batteries. Even though radar sightings were obtained, converting these into a visual sighting was difficult except under the best conditions. In 1942 the situation was temporarily improved by the introduction of the 'Leigh Light'. This was a brilliant searchlight with a flat broad beam, suitably shaped to match the characteristics of the radar search beam, and could be switched on suddenly after the presence of a U-boat on the surface had been revealed by the radar. The Leigh Light was introduced in June 1942 and was an instant success. However, by August the U-boats were afraid to surface at night and came up during the day, again making themselves visual targets. Soon, however, the enemy found an effective reply. This was to install in their U-boats a small listening receiver tuned to the A.S.V. transmissions. This allowed the U-boats to be given warning of the approach of A.S.V. equipped aircraft and at the first sign of danger submerge when, of course, they would be safe as they could not be detected. Fortunately, the British had anticipated this action and had been working on the development of a microwave A.S.V. Unfortunately there was competition for the precious microwave airborne equipment because of the rival claims of Bomber Command and Coastal Command, and it was not until March 1943 that microwave A.S.V. began to be used in Coastal Command aircraft. U-boats were now located on the surface, apparently quite unaware of their discovery, and so the attack could be more easily accomplished. U-boat sightings and 'kills' began to increase from that moment, and at the end of the year our shipping losses has been reduced to very small proportions and the U-boat menace was effectively over. It is interesting that Doenitz, the German U-boat Admiral in a speech at Weimar, during the decline of the U-boat war, admitted that the enemy (the British) had deprived the U-boat of its essential feature by means of radar, namely, the element of surprise.

However, the Germans had still another trick to play. This was their plan to produce a submarine which would operate entirely under water. Their first move in this matter was to produce 'Schnorkel' which comprised a vertical tube by means of which air is sucked in and the exhaust from the engines is discharged just below the surface of the water. The tube extends usually only a few feet above the surface and in rough seas cuts through the waves. Clearly such a small target was much more difficult to pick up than a surfaced submarine and in rough seas impossible to see either by radar or visually from an aircraft. When this development became known and its possibilities realised by the British, it was appreciated that once again the U-boat had become a real menace and had, in fact, regained all its potential danger of which it had been robbed by radar. The problem of detecting Schnorkel then became one of the most pressing with which British scientists were confronted. Clearly an object like Schnorkel, protruding

3 or 4 ft above the sea surface and having a projecting area of only a fraction of a sq metre would make only a very small target. However, it was shown that with a high-powered 10 cm radar or a medium-powered 3 cm radar, such an object could easily be detected at a considerable range. The difficulty lies in the fact that a target as small as Schnorkel was almost invariably obscured by sea returns and the main problem was therefore to increase the discrimination of the radar equipment. Methods of improving the target/clutter ratio were evolved and tried with varying success. However, Coastal Command aircraft kept the German submarines in a state of tension. The result was that the Schnorkel campaign was largely a failure and for the number of U-boats at sea, comparatively little shipping was sunk. Improved radar performances undoubtedly contributed to this situation, but the incidence of better weather also helped.

It is interesting reflecting on this situation that one move which it was thought that the enemy might make was the use of radio-absorbent materials. This is material which is used to cover possible targets to reduce the effective echoing area. One form of this is analogous to the anti-reflection coatings applied to optical lenses, and is usually referred to as 'interference absorbers'. The coating is such that a reflection is obtained from the back surface which interferes destructively with the reflection from the front surface, and so causes the resultant reflection (and therefore the echoing area) to be reduced. If this had been effectively applied to the Schnorkel, the ranges of detection would have been much reduced and perhaps, who knows, our radars would then have been useless.

LONG-WAVE A.S.V.

As already explained A.S.V. Mks. I and II operated on a wavelength of 1·5 m and used a simplified transmitter comprising triode oscillators which 'squegged'* because of the presence of high resistance in the grid circuit. The grid resistance and capacitance were adjusted so that radio-frequency pulses lasting two microseconds were obtained at intervals of

* The oscillations build up to a certain value and then stop abruptly, the process being repeated at a rate determined by the time constant of the grid circuit of the valve. A separate modulator is therefore unnecessary and although the system is not so flexible, it is certainly very simple which is ideal for an airborne radar, because of the economies in size and weight which it allows.

3000 μsec (i.e. at a pulse recurrence frequency of about 333 pulses per sec). The maximum radio-frequency peak power was 8 kW. The aerial system in the A.S.V. Mk. II consisted of separate sets of 'search' aerials on each side of the aircraft and separate 'homing' aerials on each wing of the aircraft. A motor-driven switch was connected to the two 'search' aerials and at the same time another switch operated by the same motor reversed the polarity of the signal connections to the X-plates of the C.R.O. indicator. Plate 6 shows the type of indicator employed and Fig. 20 shows a typical display. All

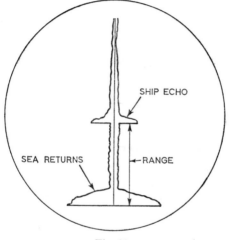

SHIP ECHO

SEA RETURNS

←RANGE

Fig. 20.

the deflections to the left of the central line represent echoes received when the aerial on the left-hand side of the plane is in use. Deflections to the right correspond, in turn, to echoes received when the corresponding right-hand side aerial is in use. If a target was sighted using the 'search' aerials, the aircraft was turned in the direction of the vessel sighted, and the system switched over to the 'homing' aerials. These aerials have a polar diagram as shown in Fig. 21 (b) and the aircraft is headed in the direction which makes the echoes received on each aerial equal. The corresponding polar diagram (Fig. 21 (a)) shows the diagram which applies when the 'search' aerials are in use.

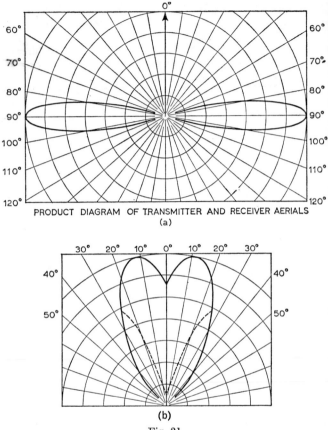

PRODUCT DIAGRAM OF TRANSMITTER AND RECEIVER AERIALS

(a)

(b)

Fig. 21.

The actual performance obtained with this form of A.S.V. equipment depended on aircraft height, state of sea (because of sea returns), operator's experience, etc., but typical figures for the maximum detectable range are 10,000 ton cargo ship ∼ 50 miles, and surfaced submarine ∼ 5 miles.

MICROWAVE A.S.V.

The original 10 cm A.S.V. (A.S.V. Mk. III) installed in a Wellington aircraft was flight-tested in January 1942. The equipment included an aerial 28 in. by 15 in. housed in a retractable turret with 360° rotation. No elevation movement was necessary as the vertical patter n of the aerial was such as to give the required coverage at the flying altitude envisaged. The transmitter power was of the order of 5 kW, the pulse length being one microsecond and the recurrence frequency 500 pulses per sec. The presentation included a 9 in. plan position indicator, and was a great step forward as it made possible simultaneous cover of the 360° around the aircraft.

Apart from the British equipments, the sharing of her techniques on microwaves naturally led to the development and production of a number of marks of microwave A.S.V. equipments in the U.S.A. Many of these were used in the European theatre.

All equipments had to be fitted with Leigh Lights and facilities for directing the light beam on the target illuminated by the radar.

Plate 7 shows the aerial scanner housing in the nose of an aircraft, whilst Plate 8 shows a typical aerial scanner out of its housing so that the relevant components can be seen. Note the waveguide feed.

LONG-WAVE A.I.

A.I. equipment was first developed on the 200 Mc/sec band (i.e. a wavelength of 1·5 m), but the equipment went through several marks and much intensive development before a satisfactory radar was evolved. The difficulty was that of obtaining a sufficiently large maximum range and a sufficiently small minimum range. It will be clear from Fig. 22 that on metric wavelengths, although a certain amount of directivity is possible, echoes will always be received from the ground when looking at an aircraft flying directly ahead. The flying height therefore decides the maximum range. Eventually, however, the Mk. IV A.I. was developed and this was installed in Beaufighter aircraft used in the Night Battle (see Chapter Two). This had a maximum range of 4 miles and a minimum range of only 600 ft.

The aerial system closely resembled that of the A.S.V. A single transmitting aerial was fitted in the nose of the aircraft and pairs of receiving aerials were fitted on the wings, one set looking up and down in a forward direction, and the other looking to left and right. Two C.R.O. displays were employed showing range and bearing of aircraft above or

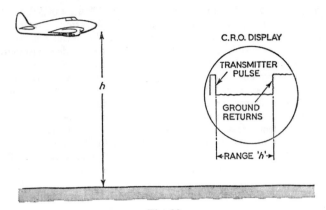

Fig. 22.

below and left or right respectively. These displays are shown in Fig. 23. Note that target echoes can only be seen if their ranges are less than the altitude of the aircraft.

There were many difficulties in using this equipment. As we have already seen from Chapter Two, the fighter aircraft needed to be vectored to a suitable location to be within A.I. radar contact, the fighter had then to close to visual sight of the target using the radar indications. After visual contact the pilot had to recognise the bomber aircraft he was chasing and shoot and shoot accurately. The displays were a little elaborate

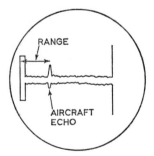

(a) ELEVATION TUBE

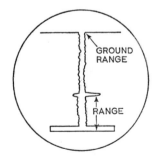

(b) AZIMUTH TUBE

Fig. 23.

to use by the pilot, bearing in mind his other duties, and a special observer was necessary to observe the radar indications and pass instructions to the pilot. It was therefore impossible to consider installing this form of A.I. in single-seater fighters. It was nevertheless this form of apparatus which was responsible for the large numbers of enemy aircraft destroyed during the 'Night Battle of Britain'.

MICROWAVE A.I.

A later form of A.I. operated on a wavelength of 10 cm. This used a 29 in. paraboloidal aerial mounted in the nose of the aircraft. This gives a beam of 10° wide which is scanned to cover from $-15°$ to $+50°$ in elevation and through 180° in azimuth. The displays are of the range-azimuth and the range-elevation type with arrangements for correlating the two sets of observations. The main characteristics were pulse power ~ 50 kW, pulse length 0·5 μsec, recurrence frequency ~ 1600 pulses per sec, azimuthal scan speed is 360 revolutions per min giving a total scan time allowing for the elevation as well as azimuthal according to a helical scan* of 2 sec, and the maximum range obtainable was about 8 miles.

Since the development of this pioneer microwave A.I. equipment, a variety of sets have been produced employing different scanning techniques. Powers of the order of 200 kW have been introduced and completely automatic search and 'lock on' radars have been developed which locate an aircraft and automatically track† it in range, bearing and elevation, supplying the information to manually or automatically controlled gun turrets.

Perhaps the most spectacular development during the war for some was the relatively small size of airborne radar equipment compared with what seemed possible when the work first started in the mid-1930's. Nowadays, with the development of transistors and microminiaturisation of all types a great deal more has been accomplished, but as a great deal more is required in the way of performance the systems have become far more complex.

* Helical scanning may be done in two ways, either a rapid scan in azimuth with a slower elevation wobble, or vice versa, the former being more usual. It corresponds to the normal television scan.
† Equipments of this sort have also been developed for ground equipments for use by land forces.

Microwave radar for navigational purposes (i.e. H$_2$S 'Home Sweet Home') is another important piece of airborne radar equipment. Some would say it was the most important piece of radar to be produced during the last war. The story of its use is so mixed up with that of other navigational aids and blind-bombing devices that a separate chapter about 'Navigational Aids' has been included in the present book: this is Chapter Four. Here, however, we might note that H$_2$S is similar to A.S.V. and essentially the same basic equipment can be used for both applications. However, aircraft using A.S.V. normally fly at low altitudes, whereas aircraft using H$_2$S normally fly at high altitudes and so the aerials designed for the individual applications need to take account of this flying height to give a satisfactory performance. It may be noted here, that as discussed more fully in Chapter Four, since the radar measures the slant range, both require a P.P.I. with a distorted time-base.

AIR EARLY WARNING (A.E.W.)

It will be appreciated from what has been said in Chapters One and Two that the effectiveness with which a radar collects information depends much on the location of the antenna. For purposes of early warning the height of the antenna is of supreme importance, as effectively with the very high frequencies straight-line propagation takes place, and so for very long ranges the radar antenna must be as high as possible. It was because of considerations of this sort that attempts were made to place early warning radars in high-flying aircraft and relay the P.P.I. information to a ground station. Some success was obtained with systems of this sort towards the end of the last war. Since then, however, the position has changed with the advent of placing satellites into orbit, so that they remain in the same position with respect to the earth. If, therefore, such earth satellites can be built sufficiently large to carry a complete radar equipment of sufficient power, it might be possible to watch over a considerable part of the earth's surface and relay the data to the ground, so as to present a picture on the ground of all aircraft and missile movements. This could be the final outcome of these developments.

CHAPTER FOUR

NAVIGATIONAL AIDS

RESPONDER BEACONS

In the very early stages of the development of radar for airborne applications, it was realised that with a small additional equipment, the radar itself would provide an excellent navigational aid. The idea was to place on the ground a responder beacon, which is a 'repeater', in the sense that it would retransmit after a very short time-interval any pulse signal

LEFT-HAND DIAGRAM   RIGHT-HAND DIAGRAM

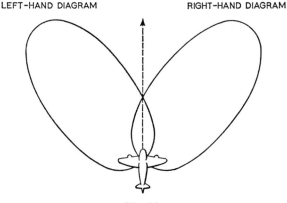

Fig. 24.

received. It is thus possible for an aircraft carrying a radar equipment to interrogate the beacon and receive back on its own C.R.O. a pulse signal, whose measured range on the C.R.O. indicates the actual range of the beacon. Obviously, if the aircraft is within range of two such beacons and the signals retransmitted by the beacons are coded in some way to allow recognition, the aircraft can measure its ranges from two fixed positions, and therefore obtain a 'fix'. In fact the early airborne radars operating on wavelengths of 1·5 m were provided with two aerials, one on each wing, providing polar diagrams as shown in Fig. 24. The signals from the two aerials were applied to the C.R.O., so that the signals received alternately on the right and left aerials produced deflections on the right and left side of the trace as shown in Fig. 25 (a). When the beacon is dead ahead the deflections on the right and left side of the trace corresponding to the beacon echo will be equal, but if the beacon is to the right or the left this will be indicated by the non-equality (see Fig. 25 (b) and (c)). This simple display therefore allowed the pilot to 'home' on to the beacon.*

It should be appreciated that the high-power radar transmitter is not really essential for triggering the beacon, and therefore for those applications where the navigational aid using beacons is the *only* facility required, a much lower-power and therefore much lighter and more compact transmitter

 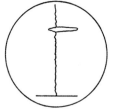 

(*a*) BEACON DEAD AHEAD   (*b*) BEACON TO RIGHT   (*c*) BEACON TO LEFT

Fig. 25.

would suffice. For this reason when independent interrogators to operate with light portable responder beacons to assist in the airborne supply and dropping of paratroops were required, this type of equipment provided a very satisfactory answer.

GEE

This is a radio navigational system, born from radar, which was used during World War II to enable our bombers to navigate over the continent. A system was needed which would operate in any weather, provide an accuracy of a few miles, and be capable of guiding them back to their bases. Furthermore, a system was needed capable of handling any number

* This will not, of course, take out drift, and if this is not done the aircraft will home to the target on a spiral course. However, operators can quickly learn to estimate drift, and compensation can be made to achieve a practically straight homing course.

of aircraft, and unable to give false information either through adverse propagation conditions or deliberate interference. Gee was chosen as meeting these conditions and was a very considerable success.

The basis of the system is that of range measurement from two fixed ground stations. The locus of a point having a fixed difference in range from two fixed point is a hyperbola, which at some distance from the fixed points approximates into a straight line. Furthermore, if the fixed difference in range is given a series of values, a non-intersecting family of curves is obtained.

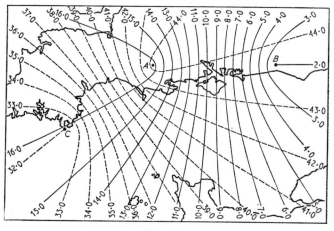

Fig. 26.

In actual practice the fixed difference in range is monitored, using radar techniques as a fixed difference in the time delays for pulses transmitted from the two stations. It is inconvenient, however, to transmit the pulses from the two stations simultaneously, since under these circumstances the time delay would change from positive to negative for different parts of the Gee field. Instead it was found more satisfactory to introduce a constant delay* between the pulses from the two fixed

* This must be greater than d/c, where d is the distance between the two stations, and c is the velocity of radio waves. It will be noted that the maximum difference in range is d/c, and in general it will be less than this quantity.

stations. The navigator could then be supplied with a Gee lattice (or chart) with the hyperbolae numbered according to the fixed difference in range which applies. Figure 26 shows a typical chart.

In practice it is convenient to have not two fixed stations, but three, one common master in each case working with a slave station (A and B, and A and C). By measuring the delay in arrival of pulses for A and C a similar set of hyperbolae is obtained intersecting the A–B family. The position of an aircraft using the Gee system may therefore be fixed by the knowledge that it lies on a particular member of each of the families of curves (A–B) and (A–C), i.e. it is at the intersection. It will be noted by reference to the previous figure which shows the Gee lattice for a Gee chain, i.e. a master and two slave stations, that a good coverage is possible and, in fact, during the last war ranges of up to 450 miles for aircraft flying at 15,000 ft were achieved.

The function of the master station is that of providing the accurate timing, not only for its own transmissions, but that of the associated slave stations as well. It is usual for the master station to transmit twice as frequently as the slaves, the sequence of the transmissions being $ABAC$, after which the cycle repeats. In order to keep the time delays always positive as already explained, the pulse from the master station A is used to synchronise the transmissions from the slave stations B and C. The pulse from A is received at B, and after being delayed the appropriate period triggers a transmitter at B, only each alternate A pulse being used. The remaining A pulses are used to trigger the slave station C in a similar way, but in order that this type of A pulse is easily identifiable (to allow the time delay AC to be recognised unambiguously), the transmitter sends out a double A pulse before the C transmissions and only a single A pulse just before the B transmissions. The arrangement of the received pulses on the C.R.O. is therefore as shown in Fig. 27. In practice, it is convenient to split the time-base into two with the second half displaced so as to come vertically under the first half as shown in Fig. 28. The A pulses then appear directly under each other, and the delays AB and AC can be measured unambiguously.

It will be appreciated that accurate measurement of the difference in ranges from the stations A and B and the stations A and C involves therefore accurate time measurements, and therefore the problem resolves itself in having an accurate electronic timer available. It would not be convenient to have a precision system of this sort on every aircraft to generate calibration markers on the time-base. Instead, it is usual to have a reasonably stable electronic oscillator to produce these time-markers, but have in addition facilities for adjusting this oscillator frequency in step with the frequency of standard calibration signals transmitted periodically by the master ground station (A in our case).

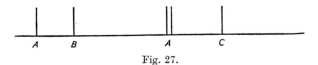

Fig. 27.

Before the Gee system was introduced it was appreciated that once the enemy realised the use that was being made of it, attempts would be made to interfere with the transmissions. It was therefore decided at the outset to be ready for this fairly certain action by the enemy by designing the equipment to be usable over a wide band of frequencies. In fact, the radio-frequency part of the airborne equipment was removable from

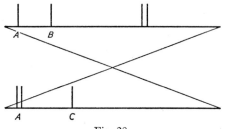

Fig. 28.

the remainder of the equipment as a 'plug-in' unit. Four separate units were produced covering the frequency bands 22–30, 45–50, 50–65 and 65–85 Mc/sec. The first two of these units were each tuned to five spot frequencies. The last two were, however, continuously tunable over the band.

During the last war Gee was used primarily by Bomber Command, but it was also used to a lesser extent for Coastal Command operations. Apart from providing the necessary navigation to ensure concentration of aircraft in time over the target, it also proved valuable in getting them home in conditions of poor visibility. When the enemy properly appreciated what was happening an intense jamming effort started. Naturally this was most serious near the target and so although the value of Gee was reduced over Germany, over the North Sea and for assisting aircraft to return quickly to their bases it was still of the greatest value. It was at this stage that the frequencies used were gradually changed making use of the plug-in units already mentioned. Naturally it was possible to spoof the enemy into believing that Gee was operating on further frequencies by modifying ground stations only, and so by changing the frequencies, spoofing and other methods resulted in the enemy having to pay an enormous cost in effort to achieve worthwhile jamming. It was also possible to save one or two special frequency bands for special operations, which with the element of surprise introduced restored the Gee cover for the particular operation, but soon after effective jamming on this new frequency started. It will be appreciated therefore that the 'Battle of the Frequencies' was an important one, not only for our reporting radars (as noted in Chapter Two), but also for our radio navigation systems.

BLIND-BOMBING AIDS

Gee provides sufficient accuracy for a general navigational aid, but it is not sufficiently good for blind bombing or for taking a photograph at night of a small target. The two-range technique already explained in the section on 'responder beacons' is obviously capable of higher accuracy. This two-range system became known as the 'H' technique and as most of the necessary timing circuits were already available in the Gee airborne equipment, the addition of a suitable transmitter transformed it into an H system. This form of apparatus was known throughout the last war as G.H.

As normally employed, the aircraft flies along one of the constant-range circles through the target. This is achieved by the operator lining up the transmitted and the received pulses with a delay set in corresponding to this range, and gives the pilot the necessary instructions to enable him to hold the aircraft on to this constant range circle. The aircraft continues to fly on this circle and when he observes pulses from the second G.H. station to be lined up with the previously calculated range of the target from this second station, he has reached the bomb-release point. This technique is illustrated in Fig. 29.

It is also possible to reverse the process by measuring the range from two ground stations and having a responder beacon in the aircraft. This is the so-called 'Oboe' system. It has the advantage over the G.H. system that the relatively complex equipment for range measurement is now all on the ground, and the equipment in the aircraft is very simple, being only a responder beacon whose only important characteristic is that of having a constant delay between reception and transmission. It has, however, the limitation that only one aircraft can be tracked at a time with each channel available. Oboe was

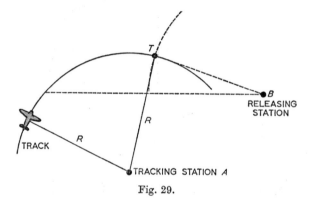

Fig. 29.

therefore employed primarily by the 'Pathfinder Force' in the last war for marking* the target for the benefit of the following aircraft. In this case the radar-responder link is used to communicate to the aircraft its position, and this is achieved by introducing a suitable modulation into the radar signals transmitted from the ground. This was a dot-dash modulation. When he is flying at the predetermined range and holding his circular track the pilot hears a steady note, and he receives a coded break in the transmission at the bomb-release point.

The accuracy of Oboe was very great indeed. On the 1·5 m system ranges of up to 300 miles were achieved at 25,000 ft with a tracking accuracy of 20 yards. In the later systems

* Visual flares were dropped on the target to mark its position for the following aircraft.

operating on a wavelength of 10 cm there were a number of refinements, including a rate of approach to track indication, which was very valuable.

MICROWAVE RADAR NAVIGATIONAL AIDS

One of the most important airborne navigational and blind-bombing aid depends on the fact that signals returned from the earth's surface vary in magnitude according to the charac-

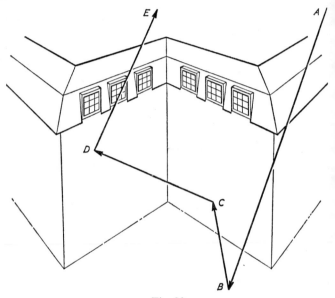

Fig. 30.

teristics of the terrain. In particular, the radar responses from water surfaces are found to be relatively weak, those from open country much stronger and those from built-up areas much stronger still. The reason for this can be seen from Fig. 30 which shows how by multiple reflections relatively strong signals can be received back from buildings, etc. A plan position indicator is used, but it needs to have what is called a non-linear time-base because the measured slant ranges have to be interpreted as ground ranges, in order that the P.P.I. shall present a map of the country over which the aircraft is flying. It will be seen by reference to Fig. 31 that the time-base sweep must not start until a time $2h/c$ (c being the velocity of the radio waves and h the height of the aircraft) after the transmitter pulse. Thereafter the sweep must move more rapidly at first and then more slowly, following the law $r = \sqrt{[(\tfrac{1}{2}ct)^2 - h^2]}$ as can be seen by a simple application of Pythagoras's theorem. Plate 9 shows a typical microwave radar (H_2S) screen and the correlation between the principal land features may be noted.

In order to obtain high resolution from such a radar equipment it is, of course, necessary to have a beam very narrow in the horizontal plane. As the physical size of the aerial on an

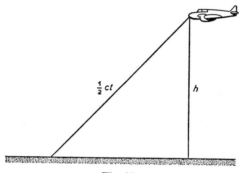

Fig. 31.

aircraft is limited by aerodynamic considerations this meant the use of microwaves. Initially 10 cm equipments were used, but in the later stages of the last war suitable 3 cm equipments were developed, and the later marks of H_2S operated on this wavelength. Much better pictures were produced and in some cases an embarrassingly large amount of detail was given. Rivers and small lakes stand out clearly and even railway lines give a noticeable return.

With the development of even lower-wavelength radars the picture quality has improved and Plate 10 shows a P.P.I. picture of this sort.

It should, of course, be appreciated that stabilisation of the aerial system is necessary so that the effect of the banking and rolling motion of the aircraft is eliminated.

CHAPTER FIVE

AIRFIELD RADAR DEVELOPMENTS

INTRODUCTION

Radar has also played an important part in assisting operations
at airfields, both during the last war and afterwards. First,
radar provided a reliable radio altimeter, which was not only
of the greatest value for aircraft which for operational reasons
needed to fly at low altitudes, but also for aiding landing
under conditions of cloud, ground mist, etc. Second, it has
provided a number of radio aids to instrument landing, and
third, it has provided means of airfield control, so that aircraft
approaching the airfield or waiting to land can manoeuvre in
perfect safety both to themselves and other aircraft. Fourth,
a great deal of delay in landing aircraft under conditions of
poor visibility is caused by the long time taken for aircraft to
be cleared from the runways. Radar provided a method of
following the movement of aircraft on the ground in all
weathers, and helps therefore to minimise delays and speed up
this type of operation. These and other applications of radar
in airfield control and operation are discussed in the present
chapter.

RADIO OR RADAR ALTIMETERS

Originally the barometric type of altimeter was much used,
and in its most sensitive form gives accurate readings of
altitude when corrected for local atmospheric pressure. Its
serious limitation is that it can give very inaccurate results
when the local atmospheric pressure is not precisely known.
The radio altimeter does not suffer from this disadvantage, and
this was one of the reasons for its success. It would be possible
to monitor the height of an aircraft by the installation of a
pulsed radar system and timing the pulses, but there is a
limitation of the minimum distance (height of aircraft) which
can be measured by this method which is determined by the
pulse width. This is because the height of the aircraft cannot
be measured on an echo until the transmitter pulse is finished
so that if the pulse width is τ, the minimum range is never
less than $\frac{1}{2}c\tau$, where c is the velocity of the radio waves. This

54

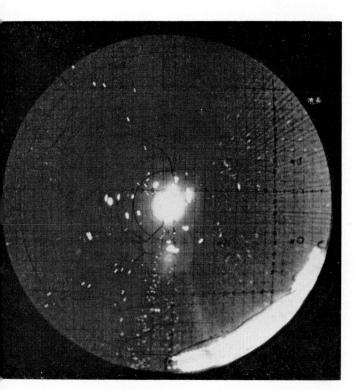

Plate 1. Plan position indicator display.

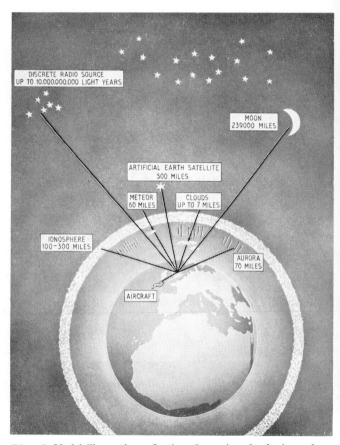

Plate 2. Model illustrating reflections from aircraft, the ionosphere, clouds, artificial earth satellites, the moon and radio noise sources.

Plate 3. Variable elevation beam (V.E.B.) operating on 1·5 m for height-finding.
(Ministry of Aviation, Crown copyright reserved)

Plate 4. Centimetric V.E.B. for height-finding.
(Ministry of Aviation, Crown copyright reserved)

Plate 5. Fighter direction station operating on 600 Mc/sec.

Plate 6 (above). Type of C.R.O. indicator used with Mk. II A.S.V.
(*Ministry of Aviation, Crown copyright reserved*)

Plate 7 (below). Aerial scanner in housing for centimetric A.S.V.
(*Ministry of Aviation, Crown copyright reserved*)

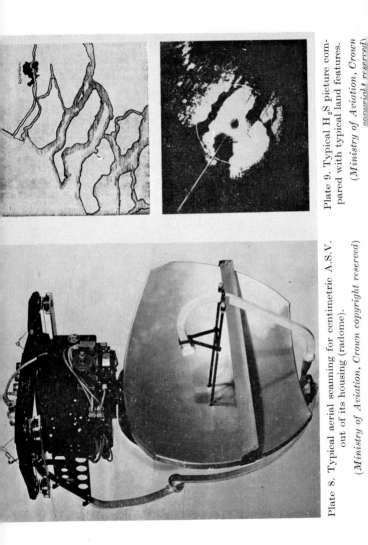

Plate 8. Typical aerial scanning for centimetric A.S.V. out of its housing (radome).

(Ministry of Aviation, Crown copyright reserved)

Plate 9. Typical H_2S picture compared with typical land features.

(Ministry of Aviation, Crown copyright reserved)

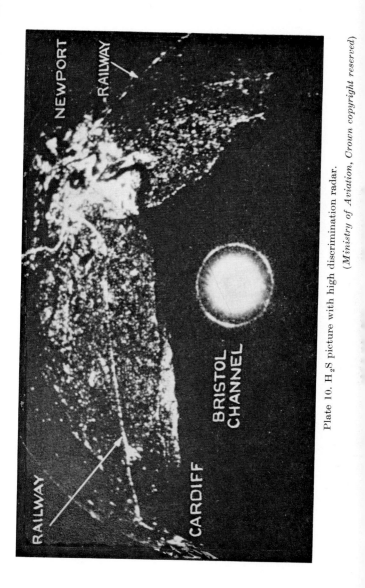

Plate 10. H₂S picture with high discrimination radar.

Plate 11. Fully steerable radio telescope at Jodrell Bank.

corresponds to 150 m for a 1 μsec pulse.* For these reasons the frequency modulation method, as used in the classical work of Appleton and Barnett (see Chapter One) was employed for this application. It will be remembered that it is inconvenient with the frequency modulation method to observe more than one target at a time, but in the case of the radio altimeter there is only a single target, namely, the ground, and so the limitation is of no consequence for this application. The frequency modulation technique has been widely applied to the problem of providing a low-reading radio altimeter, and has given satisfactory results.

In the frequency-modulation system the frequency of the transmitter is varied as shown in Fig. 32. The signals reflected from the ground are delayed by a time equal to twice the height of the aircraft divided by the velocity of the radio

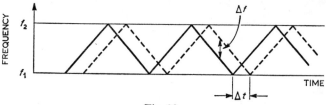

Fig. 32.

waves. In this time the frequency of the transmitter will have changed, and on mixing the returned signals with a small part of the output from the transmitter, beats will be observed after rectification. The value of this beat frequency (Δf) is given by

$$\Delta f = \Delta t \times \frac{df}{dt},$$

where Δt is the time taken for the radio waves to traverse the distance to the ground and back, and df/dt is the change of transmitter frequency with time.

In the actual apparatus the beat frequency is measured with suitable frequency-counting circuits. It may be noted that by measuring Δf and knowing df/dt, Δt may be computed†

* Later (after the war) it became possible to generate much shorter pulses, and this changed the position.

† Clearly, $\Delta t = 2h/c$, where h is the height of the aircraft and c is the velocity of the radio waves.

giving the height of the aircraft. In fact it is convenient to calibrate the frequency meter giving the beat frequency to give a direct reading of height.

B.A.B.S.

The beam approach beacon system (B.A.B.S.) was a natural development of the standard beam approach or S.B.A. with the advent of radar. S.B.A. was a c.w. (continuous wave) sys-

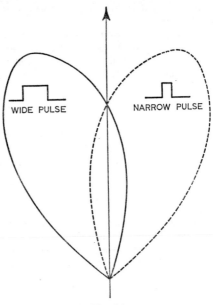

Fig. 33.

tem and defined a course with an overlapping aerial system and a dot-dash signal system to assist aircraft to approach airfields along a standard course. The advent of radar allowed them to combine this facility with a continuous indication of range. The B.A.B.S. ground equipment consists simply of a responder beacon, similar to those used for homing (see Chapter Four), together with an aerial system which lays down two overlapping field patterns as for S.B.A. These are keyed in a dot-dash sequence. The aerial system used for B.A.B.S.

comprised two half-wave slots placed in a corner reflector. The power is switched alternately between the slots simply by shorting each in turn at its centre by means of a mechanical switch. The same system is used for transmission and reception. The polar diagrams in the azimuthal plane are shown in Fig. 33, and in the transmitting mode a wide pulse (i.e. a dash) is transmitted when the left-hand lobe is effective, and a narrow pulse (i.e. a dot) when the right-hand lobe is effective as shown.

The presentation unit employed had to indicate the position of the aircraft with respect to the equal-signal line of the beam and also provide information about the range of the beacon. Figure 34 shows the type of display developed. The signals from both lobes overlap, but can be clearly seen, because of

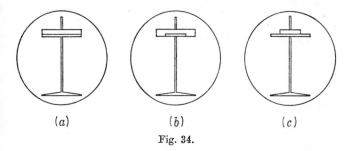

(a)   (b)   (c)

Fig. 34.

their different widths. The range of the beacon is the distance along the time-base to the echoes. When the aircraft is on the line of the runway the two signals (i.e. the wide pulse and the narrow pulse) have equal amplitudes as shown in Fig. 34(a).

With the aircraft receiving 'dashes', the display is as shown in Fig. 34(b) and the runway is on the left. With the aircraft receiving 'dots', the display is as shown in Fig. 34(c) and the runway is on the right.

GROUND RADAR FOR INSTRUMENT LANDING

Another approach to the instrument landing is to use a ground radar system. One such system developed in the U.S.A. is known as 'ground controlled approach' (G.C.A.) and is a high-precision microwave radar equipment which gives the position of the aircraft in range, azimuth and elevation. The equipment provides a processing unit which allows the position of the aircraft relative to a predetermined approach path to be displayed on the ground to allow a controller in charge of the ground station to give the aircraft continuous landing directions and 'talk it down'. This method has had a great deal of success, but has the disadvantage in this form of only being able to deal with one aircraft at a time.

AUTOMATIC LANDING OF AIRCRAFT

A great deal of work has been carried out since World War II on the automatic landing of aircraft. In England much work has been done at the Royal Aircraft Establishment, focused mainly at the Blind Landing Experimental Unit, during which time some 10,000 fully automatic landings have been made, apparently without incident using both propeller and modern jet-propelled machines. As a result, a system has been developed for the 'V' Bomber force and a variant is now being developed to meet the stringent requirements for operation in the Trident and V.C. 10 civil airliners, which is aimed to be fully operational before 1970.

The system used is a development of the S.C.S. 51, an instrument-landing system developed during the war in the U.S.A., which operates in the v.h.f. band and information is presented on a meter. The S.C.S. 51 (and the civil version known as 'instrument landing system' I.L.S.) provides the aircraft with directional, longitudinal and vertical guidance necessary to guide an aircraft in blind flying conditions to a point 200 ft to 50 ft above the end of the runway on a prescribed glide path. The glide path is developed by four high-frequency transmitters exciting four overlapping beams. The beams define a narrow pencil of radiation sloping upwards at an angle of a few degrees to the horizontal. There are, in addition, marker beacons to tell the pilot how far he is from the localiser transmitters, to indicate if the landing facility is blocked (and the aircraft must therefore follow a delaying circuit), etc.

The type of meter used in the S.C.S. 51 is of the crossed pointer type. The output of the azimuth receiver in the aircraft drives the vertical pointer of the crossed pointer indicator, and the glide-path receiver drives the horizontal pointer, so that when the pointers intersect at the centre of the dial the aircraft is on course in both the azimuthal and vertical planes. The marker receiver provides a visual and an aural warning to the pilot.

In the original application of the I.L.S. to automatic

landing, the outputs of the azimuth and glide-path receivers were applied to an automatic pilot. Other experiments have been made in which the azimuthal track to be followed is defined by a leader cable system* buried in the ground and the height was measured by a very accurate radar altimeter fitted in the aircraft, and particularly under very poor weather conditions, the 'leader-cable localiser' combined with a high-accuracy radar altimeter has provided the control signals for the final stages in the landing operation.

AIRFIELD CONTROL RADAR

During the last war short-range microwave radar equipment was tried at several Bomber Command airfields as a means of assisting airfield control, and with this experience, it is not to be wondered at, that airfield control radars are now in wide use at the great majority of airfields, both civil and military. The radar design problem is quite difficult in this case. This is because echoes from fixed objects in the vicinity of the radar normally blot out the first few miles of the trace, and it is usually targets at these short ranges which are of the first interest. Some improvement is possible in certain specific cases by careful siting of the equipment. It is also possible to use various methods of discrimination, e.g. velocity discrimination, so that echoes from fixed targets, i.e. permanent echoes are eliminated. Still another method of attack is to fit in all aircraft a small responder, and use secondary radar rather than primary radar. Secondary radar depends, as already explained, on a repeater for the returned pulse signal and not on a direct reflection from the object under observation, so that not only is the signal strength improved, but by operating the returned signal on a different frequency, the fixed echoes are eliminated. The use of secondary radar also solves the problems of identification, which can be a problem of special difficulty at airfields. The method involves the responder signals being coded in some way to provide personal identification.

At the present time both methods, namely, primary radar

* This is a cable buried in the ground carrying low-frequency a.c., and which uses the magnetic field so established to mark the path. This is not radio, because usable field strengths are only obtained close to the cable. The more knowledgeable reader will note that in this system the 'induction' rather than the 'radiation' field is employed.

and secondary radar are employed. This is largely because of the heavy organisational problem of ensuring that all aircraft are fitted with a suitable responder, and that it is in a properly serviceable condition.

PRIMARY RADAR FOR A.T.C. SYSTEMS

Radars of 600 and 3000 Mc/sec have been used in the past for A.T.C. (Air Traffic Control) systems, but there is now a large consensus of opinion that the lower operating frequency is the right compromise to adopt in this case. Perhaps the main advantage of the lower frequency is the relative immunity which its use provides to the radar against clutter due to rain precipitation. It is also necessary to make the right compromise of beamwidth and pulse length to permit optimum target identification and satisfactory resolution of the target arc of brightness on the C.R.O., satisfactorily distinguished from noise. Current opinion is that a beamwidth of 2° is a good compromise, which is the sort of beamwidth which can be obtained with an aerial of reasonable size operating on 600 Mc/sec.

It is also usual with the 600 Mc/sec radars to make successive pulses coherent, that is phase-related to a steady c.w. signal. In the ordinary type of radar, the relative phases of the r.f. wave in successive pulses vary in a random manner, because the oscillations which build up in the transmitter when the modulating pulse is applied do so from random voltages arising from thermal agitation.* The relative phases of successive pulses can, however, be made coherent by feeding a small c.w. voltage into the oscillator of the transmitter, since the oscillations in the pulse will then build up from this c.w. voltage. It follows, therefore, that all pulses start in the same phase relative to this c.w. If now the pulses reflected from a target are mixed with some of this c.w. in the receiver, the phase difference between the two will depend on the range of the target. Therefore, the echo from a fixed target will remain steady in amplitude at the output of the receiver, but the echo from a moving target, e.g. an aircraft will beat owing to the Doppler effect.

In the coherent pulse Doppler radar a method of cancellation is used in which the signals from one recurrence period are compared with the corresponding signals from the previous recurrence period. The output then depends on the difference

* In electrical parlance, this is noise.

60

in amplitude of the signals in adjacent recurrence periods. On the assumption, explained above, that the changes in amplitude are entirely due to the radial velocity of the target, it is clear that fixed echoes will not appear at the output. Echoes from moving targets will, however, show a sinusoidal beat, the peak amplitude being dependent on the radial velocity. The peak amplitude of the cancelled picture will be a maximum for a target moving an odd number of quarter wavelengths per recurrence period. This coherent pulse radar system is employed on most 600 Mc/sec A.T.C. radars, but it will be appreciated that unless a target has appreciable radial velocity it will not be detected.

It will, however, be understood from the explanation given above that it is possible for a target to be moving along a radial path and if it is moving with a sufficiently high velocity it may move a full wavelength per recurrence period, and therefore be cancelled. This trouble was not experienced until the advent of higher speed aircraft. The blind speeds of the clutter cancellation system are determined by the pulse recurrence frequency (p.r.f.) and the radar frequency. It follows that if the p.r.f. is varied, the first blind speed of the system as a whole will be the lowest common multiple of the blind speeds corresponding to the individual p.r.f.'s. Hence by using two closely spaced p.r.f.'s the first wholly blind speed of the system can be made very high.* However, the performance will still be relatively poor at certain radial velocities, and it is better, in practice, to compromise between high blind speed and optimum performance at the blind speeds corresponding to the individual p.r.f.'s. According to one designer this means that with a double system using two p.r.f.'s a p.r.f. ratio of about 3 : 2 is appropriate.

The most serious limitation of a 10 cm A.T.C. radar is that strong reflections are obtained from rain. When, therefore, aircraft require to be detected in the presence of rain clouds, serious interference with the operation of the radar can take place, and much thought has been given to methods of minimising this effect. One of the most interesting methods devised for this purpose is that using crossed polarisation. Separate antennas are used for transmitting and receiving and the polarisations are crossed, i.e. if the transmitter is arranged to transmit a vertically polarised wave, the receiver is arranged

* With p.r.f.'s of 495 and 505 pulses per sec and a radar frequency of 600 Mc/sec, the first blind speed will be at 12,500 knots.

to be sensitive only to horizontally polarised waves. With such a system weak, but nevertheless detectable, signals are obtained from targets of large and complex shapes such as ships and aircraft, but practically no signal is obtained from cloud formations, which behave as a conglomeration of small scattering particles.

Another technique which is used on 10 cm equipments is pulse compression, which is a means of reducing the effective radar pulse length without reducing the mean transmitter power. The strength of the signal from a clutter continuum (such as rain) is proportional to the size of the radar resolution cell, which is proportional, in turn, to pulse length × (range)²/ aerial gain. The use of a system to compress the pulse length from 5 to 0·1 μsec, therefore reduces the rain signal by about 50 times (or about 17 decibels)* without significant reduction in the aircraft echo. The corresponding figure for the crossed polarisation method is about 10 times (or about 10 decibels).

SECONDARY SURVEILLANCE RADARS

As already indicated the use of primary radar for A.T.C. has certain fundamental shortcomings which can only be partially overcome at the expense of complex ground equipments. Where the target is co-operative, secondary surveillance radar (S.S.R.) which requires specific airborne responders has certain important advantages. Primary radar cannot fundamentally distinguish between scattering surfaces, so that it is necessary to employ various techniques such as circular polarisation, velocity discrimination, etc., to reject unwanted replies. S.S.R. provides replies from suitably equipped aircraft only, so that the only received signal processing involved is concerned with rejecting unwanted responses from responders generated in response to adjacent interrogators, and, of course, the processing of signals which may be coded with information required for A.T.C. purposes.

One of the major problems is that of interrogation by the side lobes of the scanning aerial, because signals returned as a result of side-lobe interrogation is at the same amplitude as that transmitted in response to a main beam interrogation. For this and other reasons, it was realised quite early that it would be more satisfactory to develop S.S.R. independently

* The decibel is a dimensionless unit for expressing the ratio of two values of the power, the number of decibels being 10 times the logarithm to the base 10 of the power ratio. It is much used in radio.

of primary radar, so that proper attention could be given to the design of an interrogating aerial with adequate side-lobe suppression. The most satisfactory system involved the use of two aerial systems, one providing a control pattern and the other a directional interrogate pattern and the signal from this second aerial is shifted in time. The relative levels of the two transmissions are adjusted so that the radiated power of the first (control) pulse exceeded that of the second pulse in all azimuth directions except in the direction of the interrogate aerial main lobe where equality of amplitude is required. The responders are designed so that the relative levels of the control and interrogate pulses determine whether the responder replies or not. This provides adequate side-lobe suppression, and is recommended by the International Civil Aviation Organisation (I.C.A.O.) for Air Traffic Control systems.

A common frequency (1030 Mc/sec) is used for interrogation by all ground equipment and another common frequency (1090 Mc/sec) is used for replies by all aircraft. The purpose of the airborne responder is twofold. First, it provides a radar reinforcement signal by replying to an interrogation on one frequency (1030 Mc/sec) with the transmission on another frequency (1090 Mc/sec). This therefore results in a cheap long-range radar, free of clutter. Second, it provides an air-to-ground data link, which may be employed to transmit identification and altitude data.

It is interesting that the wartime responders used thermionic valves, but the modern versions employ transistors with, of course, some economy in size and weight and in power needed to operate them.

DISPLAY TECHNIQUES FOR AIR TRAFFIC CONTROL

Perhaps the most significant changes in Air Traffic Control in recent years are the changes which have taken place in the display systems and in the data processing. 'Raw' radar displays are provided presenting the raw data usually on a plan position indicator, but it is now usual to provide electronic markers so that data on particular aircraft targets can be extracted and presented on a special (controller's) display, together with other relevant information.

GROUND MOVEMENT CONTROL

As already explained, conditions of poor visibility can delay the clearing of aircraft from the runway, causing, in turn, delays in landing aircraft. There is therefore a requirement for keeping a check on the movement of aircraft on the ground, and radar is playing an important part in providing a satisfactory solution. The problem is difficult because it is necessary to provide relatively short-range information and, as the targets can move quickly away from the area of interest, the rate of collection of data must be somewhat higher than is usual with a radar system. It is also necessary to be able to distinguish between different targets.

Progress was made in 1955 when London Airport pioneered the use of high-definition millimetric radar to present the ground-movement controller with a detailed plan position of the airfield, showing the traffic on it. This equipment operated on a wavelength of 8·6 mm and used an aerial with a 6 ft aperture providing a horizontal beamwidth of 0·3°, horizontally polarised. The pulse length used was only 50 nanosec,* which with a beamwidth of 0·3° gave a resolution rather better than 30 ft square at $\frac{3}{4}$ mile. With this equipment it was possible to distinguish on a 12 in. P.P.I. the three tail fins of the Super Constellation, and all but the smallest aircraft could be easily identified from aspect. The Airfield Surface Movement Radar, as this radar has become known, is a considerable achievement and with the improvements in R.T. communications has allowed the ground-movement controller to use more effectively the detailed information made available to him by radar even in the densest fog.

In this radar system the aerial rotation rate is 20 r.p.m. which means that the radar information is renewed once every 3 sec. Unfortunately this information rate has proved to be too slow. Increasing the rate to 5 frames per sec, i.e. 300 r.p.m. would be satisfactory, but unfortunately introduces a flicker which imposes a severe strain on the observer's eyes. Efforts are therefore being made to increase the data rate to 16 frames per sec, which will overcome the flicker problem, but involves more difficult mechanical problems.

Rain can introduce problems at these short wavelengths. Rain attenuation is not serious, but rain can cause serious clutter, and in the latest A.S.M.I.'s being designed, use is being made of circular polarisation in conjunction with a logarithmic receiver to combat it.

The advent of the all-weather aircraft should increase the

---

* A nanosec is a millimicrosec or 10^{-9} sec.

importance of using A.S.M.I. and it seems likely that we shall see more of these millimetric radars coming into service in the next few years.

AIRFIELD TRAFFIC CONTROL

The detailed control of air traffic from take-off, direction on to the appropriate air lane to eventual touch-down, is an exceedingly complex problem. Radar plays an important part here as we have seen, but apart from the problems of instrumenting the air traffic control system, there are usually political and economic difficulties which must be considered to arrive at a satisfactory solution. The real difficulty is that parts of the air can, at times, be so full of aircraft that they saturate human abilities to co-ordinate an orderly flow of traffic. The answers at present being worked on involve many types of radar as we have seen, but this information is co-ordinated with data obtained in other ways, and perhaps the most significant change which has taken place in the last few years is the great increase in the number of controllers which are now needed to co-ordinate and direct the traffic. Thus there are ground movement controllers, flight controllers, and approach/landing controllers, to mention but some.

CHAPTER SIX

DEVELOPMENTS FROM RADAR

INTRODUCTION

There have been a number of spectacular developments from wartime radar in the post-war years. It is significant perhaps that these developments have been associated with scientists who worked on radar during the war years, and after the war were able to apply these techniques in more fundamental research. In this chapter we shall refer to two such subjects—radio spectroscopy and radio astronomy.

RADIO SPECTROSCOPY

The most spectacular development of wartime radar was the development of microwave radar—a major British contribution to the war effort at the time. It is perhaps of interest to note how developments in applied physics can sometimes initiate a major advance in fundamental research, whilst the reverse is perhaps the normal trend. Radar and the development of radio spectroscopy provide an excellent example of this. The wartime developments of radar opened up a vast unexplored region of the electromagnetic spectrum and this has been eagerly and enthusiastically worked on since this date with important results.

   The apparatus used comprises a source of microwave radiation, e.g. a klystron, and the radiation is transmitted through a waveguide, or through a resonant cavity containing the material to be analysed. The radiation is detected after it traverses the matter in the absorption cell and the attenuation caused by the matter is noted. A detecting crystal is used for measuring the power at the end of the waveguide system, and indicates any absorption of energy. The signal arising from the absorbed power is generally very small and special methods are necessary for its detection. The most popular method is to modulate the absorption by imposing a slowly varying electric or magnetic field on the matter being observed. The usual radio techniques then allow the modulation of this microwave radiation resulting from this time-variant absorption to be selected and the signal measured. With some exceptions absorption of microwave energy represents changes of the absorbing molecules from one rotational energy level to another. The absorption spectrum is characteristic of the absorbing molecules as a whole. One of the first uses which was made of this technique after the last war was the study of the fine structure arising from the inversion of the ammonia molecule. The particular feature of the ammonia (NH_3) molecule which

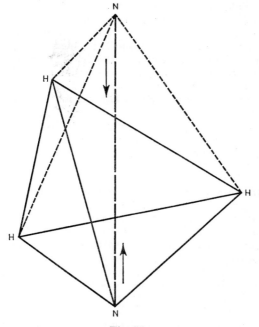

Fig. 35.

gives rise to an absorption at wavelength at 1·25 cm is its inversion, or ability to turn inside out. This is illustrated in Fig. 35. It is possible for the nitrogen (N) atom to occupy a position on either side of the plane of the three hydrogen (H) atoms, and it will, in fact, oscillate between the two positions inverting the molecule as it does so. The frequency of these molecular oscillations corresponds to a wavelength of about 1·25 cm.

The interpretation of the absorption spectra provides an understanding of the nuclear binding forces. One of the very great advantages of spectroscopy in this region of the spectrum is the very high resolution that can be obtained and the great precision available for the determination of atomic and nuclear constants.

One subject which may be specially mentioned is that of nuclear magnetic resonance, which is the name given to the resonant absorption of electromagnetic energy by a system of atomic nuclei placed in a magnetic field. The frequency of the magnetic resonance coincides with what is called the Larmor procession frequency of the nuclei in the magnetic field, and is proportional to the strength of the field. The condition for resonance is that $hY_0 = \mu H/I$, where μ is the magnetic moment* of the nuclei, I is the spin number† and Y_0 is the frequency of the electromagnetic waves to which the nuclei are subjected such that a resonant exchange of energy takes place. The constant h is a natural constant which arises in physics, known as Planck's constant and equal to $6 \cdot 624 \times 10^{-27}$ erg-sec. It is possible to rewrite the above equation as the angular frequency‡ (ω) of radiation is given by $\omega = (\mu/Ih)H = \gamma H$, where γ is ratio of the magnetic moment of the nucleus to its intrinsic angular momentum and is commonly called the nuclear gyromagnetic ratio. The nuclear magnetic resonance signal is proportional to the number of resonant nuclei present and may therefore be used as a measure of the relative abundance of a given isotope in the specimen under examination. For this reason it is finding important applications in chemical analysis, and could play a part, in the future, in process control in the manufacture of various industrial products.

Nuclear magnetic resonance studies also allow the tiny variations in the magnetic fields at different nuclear sites in a molecule to be determined. The technique can then provide

* It will be appreciated that as the nucleus carries an electric charge, its motion will produce a magnetic field. In the conditions considered the nucleus becomes uncoupled from the magnetic moment of the extra nuclear electrons and behaves independently.

† When the nucleus of an atom is considered as a single particle its total angular momentum is usually referred to as its 'spin'. The spin number is the component of spin angular momentum along an arbitrary fixed axis, and is $+ h/2$ or $- h/2$.

‡ This is a convenient concept in radio. The angular frequency (ω) is equal to 2π times the ordinary frequency.

useful information regarding the chemical structure of molecules, e.g. how the atoms are linked together.

However, apart from investigations into molecular structure, nuclear magnetic resonance can be used for the detection of much larger anomalies. Thus, the relatively strong magnetic-resonance signals such as that from protons* in water can be fairly easily detected. Furthermore, if the magnetic fields to which the sample of water is subjected are reasonably homogeneous they can be measured by proton magnetic resonance since the only quantity to be determined is the resonance frequency, and frequencies can be measured very precisely.†

With special equipment, fields as small as the earth's magnetic field can be measured. It may be noted here that in order to produce precession, the protons must be disturbed from their normal rest positions. In the case of the proton magnetometer,‡ this is achieved by subjecting the protons to a large magnetic field. When this is removed precession§ follows and the resonant frequency may be measured. It is interesting to note that the proton magnetometer has been used to good practical effect in detecting buried pottery kilns. It appears that the clay used at one time in the pottery kilns retains a small magnetic moment even after a considerable time of being buried in the earth, and at the location of the kilns introduces a small variation (an anomaly) in the earth's magnetic field which may be detected. A proton magnetometer of this sort allows field differences of 5×10^{-5} e.m.u., which is a very small fraction of the earth's magnetic field (18×10^{-2} e.m.u.) to be detected. Somewhat surprisingly even filled-in pits and ditches can be located in this way. This therefore provides archaeologists with an invaluable tool for locating sites of possible archaeological interest, without digging over vast areas—a costly and often unrewarding exercise.

* The proton is the nucleus of the hydrogen atom (H). As water has the chemical formula H_2O, proton resonances can obviously be excited in water.

† In the microwave region frequencies can be measured to one part in several million.

‡ A magnetometer is an instrument for measuring magnetic field strengths.

§ To precess, is to wobble like a spinning top that has tipped over. It is as if each particle has two axes; it spins on one and processes around the other.

A similar phenomenon occurs with electronic magnetic dipoles, but the precession frequencies involved are much larger (of the order of 10^{10} cycles/sec in fields of a few thousand e.m.u.). This is an important branch of microwave spectroscopy, which in paramagnetic solids has yielded a wealth of information on the complex interactions between magnetic electrons, the surrounding atoms or ions and the neighbouring nuclear magnetic dipoles. To obtain good resolution it is often necessary to work at very low temperatures. Good resolution is possible because the spectra, being associated with electronic moments, which are about a thousand times larger than the nuclear moments, are correspondingly more intense. This is an important advantage in the study of small numbers of magnetic centres covered by radiation damage—a subject of intense research at the present time. It also makes possible the solid-state masers,* an amplifier which has an inherently low noise, corresponding to a temperature of a few degrees absolute.† This makes it of special value in radar, radio astronomy and satellite communication.

Electron spin resonance spectrometers enable the merest traces of substances to be detected and estimated. Short-lived compounds which are created and used up during a chemical reaction are thus revealed. Furthermore, predictions can be made of how new chemical reactions may proceed and theories concerning the mechanics of chain reactions may be investigated experimentally.

The electron spin resonance spectrometer operates on the principle that an applied electromagnetic field can be modified according to the behaviour of the unpaired magnetic moment of a free electron of the substance sought. If a sample of the substance to be investigated is placed in a steady magnetic field and exposed to microwave energy of a suitable frequency resonance occurs. The resonance is detected and amplified by a sensitive microwave receiver and the information is displayed on an oscilloscope or on a pen recorder. At the moment this class of instrument is mainly used in laboratories, but in future should find use in increasing numbers in industry.

* See Chapter Ten, which discusses some of the applications of masers in radar.

† This method of defining the sensitivity of a receiver is discussed in Chapter Ten.

RADIO ASTRONOMY

The subject of radio astronomy has benefited considerably from the development of radar. It seems probable that the methods of radio astronomy will eventually pay dividends not only in pure science, but also in applied science, perhaps even in radar itself.

Radio astronomy is that branch of astronomy concerned with the study of heavenly bodies by observations of the radio waves which they emit. The subject dates from 1932 when the discovery was made that radio waves originating beyond the solar system could be detected on earth. Since that time radio waves have been used to study a broad range of astronomical objects including the sun, the moon, the galaxy and the external galaxies, and the subject is now recognised as an important and complementary part of ordinary astronomy.

It is significant that over most of the electromagnetic spectrum, the waves reaching the earth from interstellar space cannot penetrate the earth's atmosphere and the ionosphere. Of this band of wavelengths only visible light, the nearby infra-red and a portion of the radio spectrum reach the surface of the earth. The radio penetration window extends from a short wavelength limit of several millimetres, which depends on the state and humidity of the lower atmosphere, to a long wavelength limit of tens of metres, this upper limit depending upon the state of the atmosphere.

As already explained, radio waves are identical with light waves except that they have a much longer wavelength. This difference in wavelength makes radio waves difficult to focus sharply, because wave diffraction requires telescopes many times larger than optical instruments to obtain a corresponding degree of sharpness of detail, or angular resolving power. On the other hand, radio telescopes may be used to make all-weather observations on celestial regions hidden below inter-stellar dust, and planetary surfaces below permanent cloud cover.

SOLAR RADIO SPECTROSCOPY

The radio emissions from the sun can be investigated with instruments of fixed radio-frequency providing information about the variation of the intensity with time. A typical record would be of the type shown in Fig. 36. In this figure, which is somewhat idealised, a number of typical types of disturbances are illustrated.

71

To obtain more complete information it is possible to use several fixed-frequency receivers simultaneously, but to obtain more complete information about the spectrum, it is preferable to employ a special kind of spectroscope. This comprises a

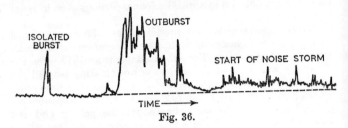

Fig. 36.

broad-band aerial connected to a receiver capable of continuous tuning over the required frequency, say, 70–130 Mc/sec. In actual operation the receiver tuning is swept through the range several times a second, and the signals produced are

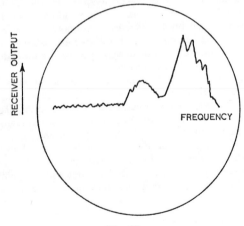

Fig. 37.

displayed on a cathode-ray tube as a signal/frequency record as shown in Fig. 37. From a sequence of such records it is possible to construct contour diagrams of bursts giving the variations of intensity with frequency and time.

The location of the actual sources of radio noise involves, in turn, a need for aerials of high gain and high resolving power. A requirement for high sensitivity means that a large collecting area is required and this is sometimes achieved with an extended array, or with a paraboloid antenna. This latter type of radio telescope is in use at the famous Jodrell Bank Station, and has the advantages of telescopes of this type of being fully steerable with ease of operation on other frequencies.

In many cases, however, the radio astronomer is interested in such high resolving power that it would be extremely costly and sometimes impossible to achieve using the paraboloid antenna. Instead many investigators have employed the interferometer technique. This can be best understood by considering two small aerials connected together. Their combined output will vary periodically as a radio source passes over them. This is the result of the interference of two transverse waves injected into the system from the two aerials. The two waves arriving at points a small distance apart will vary from being *in phase* (in which case the combined output will be reinforced) and *out of phase* (and the two wave components will cancel each other). My readers who have studied elementary optics will know that when this happens with light waves, interference results in a series of bright and dark fringes. With radio waves the same phenomenon takes place, and by measuring the visibility and timing of the fringes, the size, shape and position of the radio source may be determined. This is the principle of the radio interferometer which has been much used in radio astronomy. For some purposes interferometers of modest proportions suffice, but some experiments have been carried out, for example, using the Jodrell Bank telescope and another aerial 10 miles north of Lincoln. This provides a baseline* of over 60 miles and gives a resolving power of 1 second of arc.

Martin Ryle, Professor of Radio Astronomy at Cambridge University, who worked on radar during the war at T.R.E., has used the radio interferometer in many of his astronomical studies, and his latest and newest Cambridge radio telescope takes these ideas very much further. These ideas can be best understood by first of all explaining the 'cross' system.

* This is the distance between the two aerials.

This comprises two lines of primary antennas arranged in the form of a cross as shown in Fig. 38 (first diagram). When radio signals from both arms of the cross are received in phase there is a reinforcement in the central square shown in the second diagram of this same figure. When the signals are out of phase they cancel each other at the central square as shown in the third diagram. Hence, by subtracting one arrangement from the other a small beam is obtained which has a very high resolving power. This is illustrated in the last diagram of the series.

Martin Ryle points out that viewed from a star the earth's rotation causes one aerial to orbit the second aerial (of an interferometer) in the course of a day. Thus providing all the information is recorded and the spacing is increased in one direction, it will be possible to reproduce the effect of having a large number of aerials at various lattice points in a square

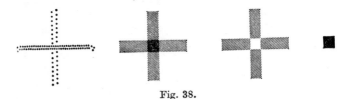

Fig. 38.

of size 'a' × 'a', where $a/2$ is the maximum spacing reached in one direction between the two aerials. Hence, he achieves the same result at very much reduced cost of an aerial covering a large area of ground. Furthermore, as each aerial receives the radiation from a relatively large region of the sky, the system has a large field of view and makes use of nearly all the information falling on its aerials.

HYDROGEN LINE RADIATION

Between the stars the density of matter is extremely small, but the astronomical distances are so great that the total quantity of interstellar material in any direction can produce observable effects on starlight as is well known. The interstellar hydrogen constitutes about half the total mass of our galaxy. It can only be seen when excited by the radiation from nearby stars. By far the greatest part of the hydrogen is in the ground state and so cannot be observed by optical means.

However, in 1951 a new field for radio astronomy was introduced by the discovery of an emission line in the radio spectrum from interstellar hydrogen. This is at 1420 Mc/sec, wavelength 21·106 cm and comes from the hyperfine structure transition in the ground state of atomic hydrogen.

FULLY STEERABLE RADIO TELESCOPES

The steerable radio telescopes have, of course, benefited considerably from the radar aerials built during the war, although they have in many cases been considerably larger and have therefore involved extremely difficult mechanical problems. The telescope at Jodrell Bank, with a paraboloid of 250 ft aperture, is still the biggest in the world, although the new radio telescope at Sydney, Australia, is a close second with a diameter of 218 ft. It is of interest to recall that the Director of the Jodrell Bank Station is Professor Sir Bernard Lovell, who as Dr Lovell, was in charge of H_2S developments at T.R.E. Dr E. G. Bowen, who heads the Australian team, was another radar pioneer and was originally in charge of the airborne radar developments in Britain from 1935 onwards.

The Jodrell Bank antenna is shown in Plate 11.

OTHER DEVELOPMENTS

As already explained, medium and long radio wavelengths cannot penetrate to the earth's surface because of the refracting ionised layers of the earth's atmosphere. However, it would be possible to receive these longer wavelengths by mounting the radio telescope on a satellite in orbit above the earth, say at a height of about 400 km. The difficulty is that a satellite of the type developed so far could only employ a small aerial. However, there is a phenomenon which makes the problem easier. This is that the ionosphere refracts the rays on to the small aerial giving it a relatively high resolving power. Hence, by choosing the orbit properly, the ionosphere and a small aerial can act together to produce effectively a very large refracting telescope.

One of the most important reasons for probing targets in outer space using radar techniques with the aid of radio telescopes is to measure distances very accurately. The basic unit of measurement in the solar system is the mean distance of the earth from the sun, which was known from optical astronomy to an accuracy of only one part in a thousand. Thus the estimate of the 'astronomical distance' could be in error by as much as 100,000 miles. The measurement of range is a fundamental problem to radar and therefore using radar to probe the moon, and the planets, should be worthwhile to improve the accuracy of our astronomical scale. This matter is further discussed in Chapter Seven.

SOME CONQUESTS OF RADAR

INTRODUCTION

Since the days of its early development, radar has been responsible for many important conquests. The most spectacular of these has undoubtedly been the bouncing of radio waves off the moon, leading to a determination of the distance of the moon from the earth. Since radar allows the very precise measurement of range, this determination is one of considerable astronomical importance. This measurement of the earth-to-moon distance was achieved soon after the end of hostilities in 1946 by Signal Corps scientists at Fort Monmouth, U.S.A., but even this has paled into relative insignificance by the measurements undertaken a few years later in probing segments of the moon's surface and even distant planets.

After the last war special efforts were made to design radar equipment for the detection of cumulo-nimbus storm centres so that aircraft could navigate to avoid such trouble spots. This has been successfully completed and many of these equipments are now in use in commercial flying. A similar development has given rise to the 'Terrain Clearance Indicator'. With the introduction of missiles in place of bomber aircraft for attacking future enemies, the radar problem has changed. It has meant redesigning the radar equipment with much increased sensitivity. This is necessary because the effective echoing area of the target has changed from 10 m² to about 0·1 m². These conquests of radar will be discussed in the present chapter, although more details of modern radar, particularly for use against military targets, will be further discussed in Chapter Ten.

DETECTION OF CUMULO-NIMBUS CLOUDS

During the last war many of our aircraft were lost by flying into cumulo-nimbus clouds. The turbulence in such clouds can, on special occasions, be so violent that the aircraft is subjected to such forces that it is literally broken up. When the matter was originally discussed at the Air Ministry, experienced 'Battle of Britain' pilots would not believe these stories, and in some official circles the reported losses tended to be put down to poor flying. Even so the position is that flying into or even near cumulo-nimbus clouds can be very dangerous, and pilots experienced in the conditions (which are, of course, more prevalent in the tropics) tend to avoid the areas of high turbulence if at all possible. I remember this very vividly on one occasion during the last war when I was flying with a highly experienced crew over Southern Siam (now called Thailand), and the pilot moved off course because of the sight (it was daytime) of an ugly cloud formation directly ahead. We tried to fly over it and even round it and both actions proved unavailing. By this time clouds were building up on all sides of us and our petrol was getting low. In the end we had no alternative but to make a 'belly-landing' on the paddy fields and trust that we should be all right! As a scientist attached to the Royal Air Force in the Far East, the problem therefore came very directly to my attention and action was taken!

The main problem was obviously at night, or in conditions of poor visibility, and so the question was—could radar provide a method of detecting turbulent cumulo-nimbus clouds as distinct from harmless rain-bearing clouds? Fortunately, cumulo-nimbus clouds are characterised by large water droplets within the cloud and, at a later stage in their development, by a concentrated fall of such droplets. Theory is a help here, and indicates that the radar scattering increases with drop size, and hence there is a probability of differentiating between dangerous and non-dangerous clouds by monitoring the radar returns. It is, of course, necessary to choose a wavelength to be selective, i.e. to receive echoes from large water droplets and not from fine droplets. A detailed analysis of the problem showed that a wavelength of about 5 cm was probably the optimum. During the later stages of the war we had 3 cm and 10 cm radar available and so everything pointed to the use of 3 cm radar for the first experiments. These experiments carried out by T.R.E. Far East were very successful. Cumulo-nimbus clouds were detected by 3 cm radar at ranges of up to 40 miles and other types of cloud, e.g. stratus and strato-cumulus did not appear to give radar returns.

Experiments of the type required on the actual cumulo-nimbus clouds are of course difficult and dangerous and it is perhaps not surprising that no definite correlation was obtained between the turbulence and the range of detection of the cloud. However, the conclusion was reached that if all radar returns from clouds are regarded as potentially dangerous and avoided, the radar navigational aid could be used successfully for ensuring safe and comfortable flying. It is interesting to note that later experiments carried out in peace-time appear to have confirmed these early results. It is therefore apparent that airborne radar of this type can be of the greatest value both in military operations and in civil flying, as it should lead to a useful reduction in the number of flights cancelled or abandoned due to unfavourable weather conditions (as has since been proved).

Many experiments were carried out at the time, and have been carried out since the war in far more detail showing that on occasions, particularly in the tropics, cumulo-nimbus cloud formations often build up from a number of different centres. Each of these centres gives a separate radar response, and it is, of course, permissible and often quite safe to fly between these centres. Again, however, this depends very much on the individual pilot's experience. Penetration through the radar-indicated gaps will give a slight turbulence, but flying round, if this is possible, will result in a more comfortable flight.

TERRAIN CLEARANCE INDICATION

Another development of airborne radar closely associated with cloud warning, because the same radar equipment is involved, is 'terrain clearance indication'. This is important, or can be important, when flying over or through mountainous country. This can be best understood by referring to Fig. 39, which shows an aircraft with forward-looking radar flying over mountainous country. If 3 cm radar is employed with two-dimensional scanning, when the aircraft is at A, the field of view will be obscured by a mass of ground returns extending from the lower sector to a fraction of the upper sector as well, indicating the high land ahead. As the aircraft continues on its flight path (as shown in the figure), it will be appreciated that at B, the clear area indicating the sky has increased.

It will be appreciated that as described the display is not differentiating between the information received from different ranges, and in fact the main problem here is one of presentation to the pilot. It will also be appreciated that in the horizontal sweeps of the aerial beam, the system can potentially detect alternative by-pass routes to the right or left of obstacles of moderate width.

Furthermore, in all these systems with forward-looking aerial systems it is essential to have a radar altimeter to be used in conjunction with the forward-looking radar. Such an altimeter informs the pilot of the exact distance between the aircraft and the terrain at 90° to the line of flight as shown in Fig. 40. Initially the frequency-modulated, continuous-wave system described in Chapter Four was tested for this application, but because of difficulties from Doppler shift during low-altitude high-speed flight, pulsed radar is now used for this

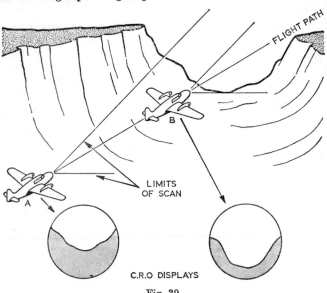

Fig. 39.

application as well. This has been made possible by the development of a short-pulse altimeter, capable of operating in the nanosecond range.* This gives satisfactory results at low altitudes (effectively 0 to 1000 m) at any speed.

A great deal of work has been done on this project by a

* A nanosec $= 10^{-9}$ sec. The minimum range which can be monitored with a pulsed radar system is $\frac{1}{2}c\tau$ (c being the velocity of radio waves $= 3 \times 10^8$ m/sec and τ being the pulse length—see beginning of Chapter Five). In the case of a nanosec pulse the minimum range is therefore $\frac{1}{2} \times 3 \times 10^8 \times \frac{1}{10}^9$, which is a small fraction of a metre.

Fig. 40.

number of different organisations to permit, amongst other things, long-range warning of very tall obstacles, the simplification of presentation systems and the improvement of automatic systems. In all cases it is convenient to feed the information from the forward-looking radar and the radar altimeter to a terrain-avoidance computer which provides the pilot with optimum flight-path information.

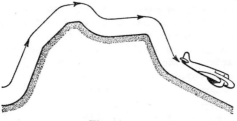

Fig. 41.

Apart from the obvious civil application of terrain-clearance indicators to allow the detection of hazardous surface objects with sufficient clarity and sufficient time to permit alternative alterations of the flight path, terrain clearance methods are of value in the military case to allow heavily loaded aircraft to fly at low altitudes and follow the contours to avoid radar detection and destruction by radar-guided missiles. This is illustrated in Fig. 41.

As already mentioned, one of the first big successes of radar after the war was the reception of pulsed signals after reflection from the moon. This involved a time lapse of $2\frac{1}{4}$ sec, and this was the first occasion in which a physical distance outside the earth's atmosphere had been directly measured, and as has been said on many occasions the fact that such a measurement is possible may have a profound effect on the philosophy upon which our theories of the universe are based.

The first radar return from the moon was an echo on the U.S. Signal Corps radar at Fort Monmouth in 1946. This echo indicated a range of 238,000 miles, and the moon was illuminated with an antenna with a beamwidth of 2°. The moon subtends an angle of $\frac{1}{2}$° as seen from the earth, and so clearly no angular resolution was possible. However, large antennas are now available with beamwidths of about 0·06° and so the fine detail can be revealed by experiments with these larger systems. It is interesting to note, however, that the moon exhibits certain motions which cause its various parts to appear to move at different relative velocities with respect to an observation point on the earth. It is therefore possible to use a coherent pulse radar system and look for this velocity difference using the methods discussed in Chapter Five. This involves extracting the data from the radar echoes received from the moon using computer signal-processing techniques, which store the radar returns obtained over several minutes and then re-examines these returns for specific characteristics. Radars with these combined information-gathering possibilities are one of the most significant developments of modern radio astronomy, and in the case of the moon experiments it has been possible to identify the echo received from a single crater on the moon's surface only 55 miles in diameter.

The Americans and the Russians established contact with the planet Venus using radar at about the same time. Mallory and Galomb (U.S.A.) received Venus echoes using a planetary radar system from March to May 1961, and obtained a value of 149,598,500 km for the astronomical unit,* which they claim is possibly accurate to $\pm$ 500 km. The rotation of Venus was determined by spectral analysis of the data as about 225 days. Their radar operated on a frequency of 2388 Mc/sec.

The present author was fortunate enough to attend a meeting

---

* This is the distance of the earth from the sun.

where these results were presented. At the same meeting the Soviet scientist V. A. Kotelnikov gave an account of his experiments in making radar contact with Venus. In the discussion of the Russian contribution, the American authors said their first reaction in studying the Soviet-press release on Venus radar in *Izvestiya* on 16 May 1961 was to congratulate them on the discovery of a new planet, as it was surely not Venus that had been observed as it was 30,000 miles closer and rotating 25 times faster. However, as the discussion proceeded it was seen that the two sets of observations were not very much out of agreement, and the confusion arose because of the different methods of expressing the results.

TRACKING OF BALLISTIC MISSILES

It has already been explained in Chapter Two how the original C.H. radars were used for tracking the German V-2 missiles during the last war, and using the data to predict the likely trajectory and the point of attack. It was also possible by extrapolating the trajectory backwards to determine the firing point. Since the last war much research has been carried out on ballistic missiles and it is now apparent that future wars, if we have to have them, are likely to be fought in the air with missiles rather than with manned aircraft. It is therefore of interest to inquire about the visibility of such missiles to radar as compared with bomber aircraft.

If we assume that the projectile is some 100 ft long and 3 ft in diameter, weighing 30–40 tons when fired, it might be expected that the signals received from a ground radar station would be comparable with those received from a moderately small to medium-sized aircraft. On the other hand, a more detailed mathematical analysis assuming an accurately cylindrical form leads to the result that a very large signal would be returned if the axis of the cylinder were perpendicular to the direction of the radar station. If, however, the angle departs slightly from a right angle, the signal returned falls off rapidly, and at angles of, say, 50–70°, the returned signal is much less than that from an aircraft, or a rough obstacle of the same size as the missile. This is because the missile is many wavelengths long and the radiation is therefore sharply beamed. Taking this and other matters into consideration, e.g. that a number of boosting stages may be used which are subsequently jettisoned in the case of the long-range missiles, the effective echoing area may be as low as $0\cdot1$ m², as compared with about 10 m² for a manned bomber of the type used in the last war.

It may be asked whether the hot-exhaust gases or other hot exhaust from the rear of the missile would assist detection by contributing to the effective echoing area. After all, the reader may say, ionisation in the upper atmosphere—the so-called ionosphere—is sufficient to reflect radio waves and allow the propagation of radio waves round the curved surface of the earth. In fact whether this is so or not depends to a large extent on the temperature of the gases emitted and their composition, and in the case of the V-2 missile the contribution of the hot ionised gases in the exhaust was only a small fraction of one per cent of the total echoing area.

Apart from the reduced echoing area of the targets, their very high speeds make it essential that they be detected at very long range, which means up to 2000 miles (as compared with about 200 miles on bomber-aircraft targets which sufficed during the last war). As explained in more detail in Chapter Ten, the modern radar stations which are now with us have a sensitivity of about a million times that of the systems used with such success in the last war. One of the latest examples is the giant station at Fylingdales, Yorkshire. This comprises three large glass radomes* housing the antennas 84 ft aperture and weighing 150 tons. These continually scan the skies and feed echo information into a giant data processing system, which assesses the nature of the target from the echo characteristics, evaluates the threat, measures the speed of the target (or targets) and predicts the time and place of descent. There is also an elaborate monitoring system so that every part of the system is under perpetual and automatic surveillance. Any faults in the system are duly indicated, and in such a way that the action called for by the maintenance engineers is clear.

MIGRATION OF BIRDS

During the last war echoes were sometimes observed on the C.R.O. indicator on occasions when it was known that no aircraft or surface craft was in the locality indicated. Naturally there were many stories passing around as to the origin of these 'mystery' echoes, but at least in some cases it can now be stated that these echoes were almost certainly due to flocks of birds. Initially it was not appreciated that flocks of birds could be detected by radar, but this is definitely the case, and

* This is a contraction for radar domes.

some radar operators at the higher-frequency radar stations regularly observed the flight of seagulls passing near the station. Since the war many ornithologists have found radar useful in their work of studying the habits of bird life, the migration of birds, etc.

David Lock (Director, Edward Grey Institute, Oxford University) has carried out many migration studies using radar. With centimetric height-finding equipment he has been interested in the flying heights of migrant birds. Apparently the common Passerine winter visitors to Britain migrate below 5000 ft, and they tend to fly higher in spring than in autumn, and higher by night than by day. Occasional individual birds were recorded up to 14,000 ft. Most migration occurs a few thousand feet above the earth's surface, and this is the height to be expected on general grounds, for in most cases it is high enough to keep the birds clear of a rise in terrain and above ground mist. Apparently also the birds maintain a steady height for the major part of the flight.

The experience of airmen indicates that it is extremely hard to maintain a constant height by visual means under any conditions, and particularly over sea and at night. How then do migrant birds maintain constant height? This is one of the problems thrown up as a result of the more exact information which radar is now providing to the ornithologist.

APPLICATIONS OF INCOHERENT SCATTERING

We have already mentioned the role of the ionosphere in facilitating long-distance radio communication. A proper knowledge of the variation of the electron density with height above the earth's surface is essential to the engineer for successful h.f. communication, and also to take account of the effect of the ionosphere on the radio tracking of satellites and rockets. It is interesting that sounding of the ionosphere to determine the electron density is now made using radar. A high-power metre-wave radar on the earth's surface is directed upwards and very weak scattered echoes are seen from the ionised part of the earth's atmosphere. These 'incoherently scattered' echoes are returned from the whole range of heights at which ionisation occurs, the echo power coming from any particular height being proportional to the density of free electrons at that height.

It is of interest to note that this new technique provides much more information than the original 'Appleton' like measurements using pulses of waves of frequency low enough to be totally reflected by the ionosphere. With the incoherent scattering technique, a frequency is employed well above that at which ionisation reflects or refracts radio waves, so that the transmitted beam of energy passes, substantially without change, right through the atmosphere. However, the free electrons excited by the electric field of the wave are, in turn, aligned with this electric field and re-radiate energy with a dipole directional pattern, and it is this scattered energy which may be detected with a sufficiently sensitive receiver on the ground.

It is instructive to consider the basis of the method. If the transmitting and receiving aerials are oriented to look at the same piece of the ionosphere, and the beams have a solid angle Ω, the cross-section of the beam at a range r is $r^2\Omega$. If the pulse duration is τ, the echoes on its display will come from a range interval $\frac{1}{2}c\tau$,* and so the total volume contributing the echoes is $r^2\Omega\frac{1}{2}c\tau$. The number of effective electron scatterers is obtained by multiplying this volume by the volume density of free electrons, and is thus proportional to r^2N. The echo power received from a single electron target varies as σ/r^4 (where σ is the scattering cross-section of a free electron), so that, taking account of the r^2 dependence of the number of electrons simultaneously illuminated, the echo power will vary with range as $N\sigma/r^2$.

Various experimenters have used the above method to determine the absolute value of N and its variation with height. Measurement of the spectral width of the responses gave some unexpected results, not initially anticipated by the theory, and relatively recently it has been shown that the actual echoing cross-section† which is appropriate varies with time of day, and depends on the absolute temperatures of the electrons and ions in the ionosphere. The method is now therefore showing promise of providing measurements of electron and ion temperatures, identification of ions present, etc. It is very exciting!

HELPING THE BLIND WITH SOUND WAVES

As still a further application, it may be mentioned that successful experiments have been made recently on using

* See Chapter One.
† These developments call for a super-sensitive radar, and amounts to being able to detect something of the order of size of a sixpence at 300 miles.

radar for providing guidance for blind people. The frequency of the radiated signal is changed steadily from 60 kc/sec to 30 kc/sec in 0·5 sec. An echo is received from an obstacle at, say, 30 ft after a time of travel of 0·055 sec (ultrasonic waves), during which time the outgoing frequency, 60 kc/sec, has changed to 56·7 kc/sec. By mixing and rectifying, a difference frequency of 3·3 kc/sec is heard, which is proportional to the distance away of the obstacle. The sponsors of the scheme visualise the final form of the apparatus as a hand torch weighing about half a pound with batteries. The device is surprisingly sensitive and will detect a 1 mm vertical wire at 4 ft.

CHAPTER EIGHT

TRACKING OF ARTIFICIAL EARTH SATELLITES AND SPACE PROBES

INTRODUCTION

One of the important parts played by radio and radar in space research is the tracking from the ground of the vehicles which carry the research instruments into space. This is also of even greater importance with the advent of the man-carrying space vehicles, because of the greater need for accuracy of orbit data so as to be able to predict future positions of the vehicles.

In many ways this is similar to the original detection of aircraft problem. Optical methods when they can be employed are capable of greater precision, but the advantages which applied when radar was originally put forward still applies, of which the main one is that of providing more continuous observation, since it is not limited by cloud cover or lack of solar illumination. Radio and radar methods have also the advantages of allowing observations to be made on satellites, which because of their size and distance would give signals too weak for tracking by optical methods.

There are many systems for the tracking of earth satellites. Some depend on the presence of a small transmitter in the satellite itself and on accurate direction finding on this signal using interferometer methods. Other (radar) methods depend on the satellite playing the purely passive part of simply reflecting a radio-frequency beam in which it is illuminated. In some cases the range obtainable with the radar method has been improved by installing a small pulsed transmitter in the satellite (i.e. a responder) which may be triggered by the radar ground station transmitter. This therefore involves the principle of 'secondary radar'.

It will be appreciated that if the power supply in an earth satellite or a space probe fails, only the primary radar will provide information. It will be seen therefore, that a good case can be made for the use of a combination of tracking systems being available for use with any one project.

The main methods are

(1) determination of directional information using the v.h.f. signals transmitted by the satellites and interferometer techniques;

(2) use of a narrow beam steerable aerial as a receiver using v.h.f. signals as before, or employing the steerable aerial both for transmission and reception and employing radar techniques to determine both range and direction of the satellite or space probe, with or without a responder.

(3) utilisation of the Doppler frequency shift of the satellite signal for the determination of range and velocity.

Radio waves are, of course, used in the satellite for a number of purposes. These are (1) for tracking purposes for the determination of the orbit; (2) for finding out about the ionosphere through which the radio waves travel; and (3) for sending back by telemetry the information gained by the automatic measuring equipment in the instrument satellites.

INTERFEROMETER TECHNIQUES

An interferometer consists (as explained in Chapter Seven) of two aerials separated by several wavelengths and connected to a recorder so that the output oscillates sinusoidally as the difference between the paths of the waves from the satellite to the two aerials varies. When the record passes through a zero the path difference is known to be an odd number of half-wavelengths, so that the satellite is known to be on one of a series of confocal hyperboloids of revolution with the two aerials as foci. Successive zeros on the record correspond to the passage of the satellite across successive hyperboloids. The actual track can be identified from the geometry, although at the expense of some complication in the equipment the ambiguity can be removed. Figure 42 shows the layout of the aerials. It will be noted that, in practice, two pairs of aerials are used. Horizontal aerials are commonly employed, and the spacing between them is ten to fifty wavelengths. Simultaneously, observations on the two pairs of aerials allows the azimuth (θ) and the elevation (α) of the satellite at a given time to be computed. However, there is the ambiguity already mentioned. This is avoided by making simultaneous observations on a second system with a shorter base-line of one or two wavelengths in which the alternative directions are more widely spaced, and the ambiguity is quickly resolved.

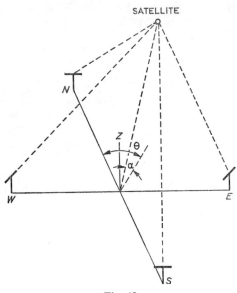

Fig. 42.

DOPPLER METHOD

Another method of radio observation of earth satellites makes use of the Doppler effect. As the satellite passes close to an observer the frequency of the waves received from it alters.* This is shown in Fig. 43. The limiting frequencies, at the two ends of the record, represents the Doppler shifts when the satellite is moving straight towards the observer and straight away from the observer, and from the difference between them the velocity can be determined. It should be noted that the actual shape of this curve depends on how quickly the line-of-sight velocity changes and therefore on the distance of closest approach. There are several methods of using the Doppler system of monitoring. Thus, if the distance of closest approach is determined for the same track, it is possible to deduce

---

* The reader may be more familiar with the Doppler effect with sound waves and that the fact that a sounding body changes its apparent pitch when it passes the observer with considerable velocity. Thus, the whistle of a railway engine appears to become considerably lower in pitch as it passes the observer.

the position of the track in space and hence determine the actual orbit. Another very satisfactory method is to use only one observing point and make observations on successive transits of the satellites. It should be appreciated that the time of rotation in the orbit depends upon the size of the elliptical path followed, but is of the order of $1\frac{1}{2}$ hr if the satellite is at a height of a few hundred kilometres. However, the earth rotates on its own axis inside this orbit once every 24 hr, therefore an observer at a given place on the earth

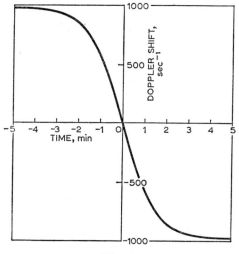

Fig. 43.

moves relative to the orbit. It may be seen, for example, by reference to Fig. 44 that the observer is carried round the line $ABCD$ once per 24 hr, while the satellite goes round its orbit PQR once, say, in $1\frac{1}{2}$ hr. It will be clear from an examination of this figure that when the observer is near B the satellite will pass over or near him on a few north-going tracks, and later, when he reaches D, it will pass over or near him for a few south-going tracks.

We may now examine Fig. 45 which illustrates this alternative method of determining satellite tracks using only one observing station. The position of nearest approach is found

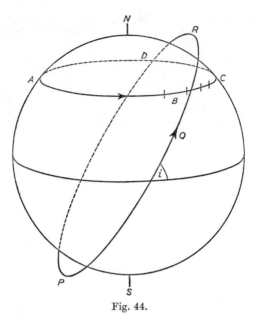

Fig. 44.

by measuring the distance approach (see previous figure—Fig. 44) on successive transits when the observing station (relative to the satellite's orbit) is first at A and then B, the relative motion being due, of course, to the earth's rotation.

In concluding this discussion of the radio (non-radar) methods, it should be made clear that the tracks deduced from radio observations are not sufficiently accurate for many purposes, and it is therefore necessary to supplement them

Fig. 45.

with more accurate visual or radar observations. However, the radio observations are valuable and often essential to indicate where the search should be conducted with the more accurate equipment.

RADAR TRACKING

In England the Jodrell Bank experimental station with its 250 ft radio telescope operating on frequencies of 36, 100 and 120 Mc/sec has been used for the radar tracking of earth satellites. The Royal Radar Establishment's 45 ft radio telescope operating on a frequency of 3000 Mc/sec has also been employed for the same purpose.

Perhaps the main function of radar tracking is that of position measurement on the final stage of the launching vehicle so that the injection parameters for preliminary orbital calculations can be accurately determined. The Americans now seem to be relying on radar stations as the primary means of tracking manned vehicles. Apparently the main reason for this is that at this stage, at least, such satellites will have orbital lifetimes of only a few revolutions, and radar methods are capable of providing the necessary information on the actual orbits with the shortest possible delay. In the case of unmanned vehicles the tracking data are required for prediction purposes.

At the present time the Americans are using a number of radar-tracking stations to provide round-the-world coverage. Their system includes a main control centre incorporating a central computing and communications organisation, including suitable telemetering receiving stations, so that all the data available regarding the position of the satellite can be co-ordinated and correlated to enable the computers to be used to calculate the orbit-data, predict future positions of the satellite, etc. The data are also available at the actual radar stations to allow satisfactory target acquisition, because most of the radars employed are narrow-beamed devices, and without satisfactory input data, they might not, in many cases, be able to pick up the radar signals and undertake their tracking assignments.

Perhaps the most accurate radar used in this system is the F.P.S.-16, which provides azimuth, elevation and range data on the target in analogue and digital* form, and the tracking

* The use of digital data allows more accurate computations and simplifies the transmission of the data.

accuracies are of the order of 0·1 milliradian in angle and 5 m in range. The main characteristics of this system are summarised in the table below.

F.P.S. radar characteristics

Frequency	5400–5900 Mc/sec
Pulse power	250, 1000 kW
Pulse width	0·25, 0·5, 1·0 μsec
Repetition rate	160–1707 pulses/sec
Antenna diameter	12 ft
Antenna gain	44·5 dB
Beamwidth	1·1°
Receiver noise figure	9–11 dB
Bandwidth	1·6 and 8·0 Mc/sec
Tracking rate range	7300 m/sec
Tracking rate angle	0·7 radians/sec azimuth
	0·54 radians/sec elevation
Feed	4-horn monopulse

In some cases it is more convenient to install at each narrow-beam radar for accurate tracking of target vehicles a wider-beam radar. This avoids the time-delay in the acquisition of the target by the main system. In the American system, this uses a 20° beamwidth and pointing data are automatically transmitted to the main radar. In general, it is usual to transmit the readings of the azimuth, elevation and range from the radars to the computing centre where the orbit calculations are carried out in 'real' time, so that information in the form of predicted 'look angles' can be transmitted to the succeeding stations before the satellite comes within their range.

CHAPTER NINE

RADAR TECHNIQUES AND NUCLEONICS

HISTORICAL DEVELOPMENT

After the last war there was a tremendous drive in the attempt
to exploit nuclear energy for the benefit of mankind. As most
readers will be aware this drive was a great success. Nuclear
power plants generating electricity are in operation in many
parts of the United Kingdom, and indeed in many parts of
the world. Nuclear energy is also being employed in the
operation of propulsion units, notably in submarines, and this
use will increase. Radio isotopes, one of the by-products of
nuclear energy, are being used on a large scale. Sales of radioactive products from the Radiochemical Centre at Amersham
(U.K.A.E.A.) in 1962–3 amounted to nearly one and a half
million pounds sterling, of which more than 50% represented
export sales. But it is the savings effected by the use of radio
isotopes, rather than the direct sales, that the success should
be judged in this case. Radioisotopes are now firmly established in process control for use in nucleonic thickness gauges,
density and level gauges, whereas larger sources of radiation
are being employed for industrial processing and for radio-
graphic inspection. In medicine, radioisotopes have found
many applications. As a diagnostic tool, radioisotopes may be
administered orally or intravenously, and their subsequent
course traced in the patient's body, or in blood or urine
samples.

All these projects involved special instrumentation problems,
and a great deal of electronic equipment and electronic
measuring apparatus had to be designed and manufactured
as an important part of these nuclear energy programmes. The
developments of war-time radar helped very considerably
here.

In the United Kingdom it was appreciated at a very early
stage that electronic techniques would play an important
part in the development and utilisation of nuclear energy.
At the end of the last war* many of the young scientists and

* This was at the Telecommunications Research Establishment,
Malvern (T.R.E.), in the department headed by the present author
as Superintendent. It is now the Royal Radar Establishment.

engineers, who had played a part in the development of war-time radar, were switched by official decision to applying electronic techniques to the problems of nuclear energy. This ensured that a strong electronics team was immediately available to tackle the new problems, and that the latest electronic techniques were applied to these problems. The effects of this decision were far-reaching.

One team at T.R.E. applied their knowledge of waveguides and microwave radar to the design of a particle accelerator,* and succeeded in producing the first travelling-wave linear accelerator in the world. This was the forerunner of many linear accelerators used for nuclear physics studies, for the determination of nuclear constants of materials being considered for the construction of nuclear reactors, and for radiotherapy in hospitals. These machines are also being used now for food sterilisation, sterilisation of medical equipment, irradiation studies, etc.

A second team at T.R.E. became interested in the theoretical ideas on a new form of particle accelerator proposed by McMillan in the United States and Veksler in the U.S.S.R. This machine was designated the synchrotron. The T.R.E. team modified a betatron and added suitable radio-frequency equipment and succeeded in demonstrating for the first time that synchrotron action did work. They made, in fact, the world's first synchrotron and succeeded in getting it to work. This was the forerunner of many machines, some small, some large and some very large, for nuclear physics research and, in the case of the more modest machines, for radiotherapy.

Still another team at T.R.E. applied their knowledge of electronic pulse circuits developed in connection with war-time radar to the various problems of assaying and identifying radioactive materials. This was an especially fruitful field, because the wartime techniques were directly applicable to the problems on hand. In radar, short pulses of electromagnetic radiation are used to illuminate a distant aircraft and an electronic circuit is used to measure the time taken for the pulse to be received back again at the radar set, after reflection or scattering by the aircraft. This time is obviously related (as already explained in earlier chapters) to the range of the target aircraft and the method provides a convenient method

* This is a machine for accelerating particles (e.g. β-particles) to high energies for bombarding nuclei and studying nuclear reactions. In the vernacular it is an 'atom smashing' machine.

of ranging. It may be noted that the radar system involves, amongst other things, an apparatus to generate the short pulses of electromagnetic energy (usually designated the transmitter), and a receiver which receives, amplifies and times the arrival of these pulses after their passage to the aircraft and back to the receiver.

In radioactivity measurements a radiation detector is employed. There are several different types, but in one type —the gas counter—discharges take place producing a pulse of current each time a particle or an γ-ray photon enters its sensitive volume. To determine the quantity of radioactive material present in the sample under investigation it is necessary to measure the rate of arrival of the particles or photons using the radiation detector and suitable auxiliary electronic equipment.

This is accomplished by measuring the pulse counting rate, using again basic circuits which were developed for wartime radar. To identify the radioactive material in the sample it is necessary to measure the amplitude distribution* of the pulses obtained from the discharges of the detector, and again the necessary electronic circuits which are used, owe much to the basic circuits of radar.

In these early days, immediately after the last war, many instruments, or 'tools of the nuclear age' were developed, e.g. radio-assay meters, pulse-amplitude analysers (sometimes designated as spectrometers, as they measure in conjunction with a suitable particle or radiation detector the energy spectra), pulse amplifiers, counting-rate meters, radiation monitors for health physics measurements, etc. The success of this early work cannot, however, be attributed only to the fact that the team contained amongst its numbers many well versed in the electronics techniques of wartime radar. One other important contributory factor was that some members of the team had been nuclear physicists before the war, and had been directed into radar work at the outbreak of hostilities. These members were able to contribute a great deal on the user aspects of the required designs, and thus ensure that the instruments designed were not only good from the point of view of electronic design, but also convenient for the purpose on hand as well.

The result of this early work at T.R.E. was that when the

* This is the energy spectrum. As different radioactive materials have a different energy spectra this is a useful method.

Atomic Energy Research Establishment (A.E.R.E.) was set up at Harwell in 1946 there was a strong electronics team in being, and many nuclear-measuring instruments in a prototype or near-prototype stage. The T.R.E. team did, in fact, form the nucleus of the Electronics Division at A.E.R.E., Harwell, and gave it a very fine start.

RADIOACTIVATION ANALYSIS

Radioactivation analysis is a method of elemental analysis by irradiating the sample, usually with neutrons* and observing the radioactivity induced. Since extremely minute quantities of radioactivity can be detected and measured relatively easily, this proves to be a very sensitive method of analysis. It is now being widely used in chemical laboratories and is gradually invading the field of industrial control. It is being used particularly for the estimation of small quantities of unwanted elements in certain industrial products. These unwanted elements can be made radioactive, and therefore detectable, by neutron bombardment. The properties of germanium and silicon, important materials in the electronic industry, are gravely affected by small impurities, down to one part in a thousand million. Radioactivation analysis can be employed, for example, for the determination of the amount of arsenic and copper in silicon down to one part in ten thousand million, because these elements are strongly activated by thermal neutron bombardment, whilst silicon is not.

The basis of neutron activation analysis is to irradiate the material (or a sample of it) with neutrons with, in general, the production of a radioactive nuclide† which decays with the emission of γ-radiation or β-particles. A detector can be arranged which responds selectively to this radiation, whilst giving no response to radiation of other types and other energies (corresponding to other elements), so that the detection of radiation of the appropriate type and energy allows recognition and estimation of the particular element of interest in the sample. Furthermore, since the activity decays with a

* A neutron is a nuclear particle having no electric charge and the approximate mass of a hydrogen nucleus. It is found in the nuclei of atoms and plays a vital part in nuclear fission.

† A radioactive nuclide is a nuclide which spontaneously disintegrates with the emission of particles or radiation or both to form a daughter product, which may be stable nuclide or a radioactive nuclide.

characteristic half-life,* it is possible to measure the decay characteristics as a further means of identifying, or confirming the identification of the element in question.

It may be instructive to consider a specific example. We will consider the determination of arsenic. Ordinary arsenic is ^{75}As, the index 75 indicating that the atomic weight of the arsenic nucleus. If this is bombarded with thermal neutrons (that is neutrons of thermal energy), the neutron is captured by the ^{75}As nucleus to form ^{76}As, which is a radioactive form of arsenic with an atomic weight of 76. The complete reaction can be written down in the 'shorthand' form—

$$^{75}\text{As}(n, \gamma)^{76}\text{As},$$

which represents that when ordinary arsenic (^{75}As) is bombarded with neutrons, the neutron is captured, and the compound nucleus (^{76}As) in de-excitation emits a γ-ray. The product nucleus formed (^{76}As) is radioactive and decays with a half-life of 26·7 hr emitting a γ-ray of 0·56 MeV† and β-particles of various energies to form selenium (^{76}Se), which is stable. It is possible therefore to monitor the 0·56 MeV γ-ray after neutron-irradiation as a means of determining the arsenic content of the sample. The sample can be irradiated with neutrons conveniently by placing it in a nuclear reactor for a time.

In general, such reactors are operated continuously, and the sample injected into the neutron flux and at the end of the irradiation period ejected into a monitoring position some distance from the reactor site by pneumatic means. This is because, with radionuclides of short half-life, it is essential that there should be the minimum of delay between the end of the irradiation period and the beginning of the measurement time, since the activity is decaying during this time.

In very recent times interest has become centred on radioactive nuclides of very short half-life. For such nuclides it is an advantage to use a 'pulse' method. The pulsing is achieved by rapid removal of the main control rod from the reactor core, making the reactor supercritical. This causes the neutron

* The half-life is the time in which the radioactivity has decayed to half its initial value. If this value is $t_{\frac{1}{2}}$, then after a time $t_{\frac{1}{2}}$ only half the activity remains. After a further time $t_{\frac{1}{2}}$ (making $2t_{\frac{1}{2}}$ altogether) only a quarter of the initial activity remains. After a time $nt_{\frac{1}{2}}$ the activity remaining is $(\frac{1}{2})^n$ of the initial activity.

† The MeV is a million electron volts and is a unit of energy.

flux and the power level to increase promptly at a great rate, reaching a peak usually in a matter of milliseconds. The excursion promptly quenches itself, however, because of the rise of temperature and the negative temperature coefficient of reactivity of the fuel (usually the isotope of uranium known as ^{235}U). It is possible in this way to operate a reactor at extremely high-peak flux level (higher by several orders of magnitudes) compared with the flux level for continuous operation. For radioactive nuclides of half-life comparable with the pulse length this increases the activity induced in direct proportion to the increase in flux level and therefore increases the sensitivity of this method of analysis also in this ratio. The penalty one has to pay is that the repetition rate cannot be very high, which limits the number of samples which can be handled in a given time.

CAPTURE GAMMA-RAY ANALYSIS

It will be remembered that in discussing neutron activation analysis we referred to the neutron capture reaction

$$^{75}As(n, \gamma)^{76}As$$

and it was noted that the arsenic content of the sample could be determined by monitoring the amount of ^{76}As produced. This was performed by monitoring the γ-rays emitted by ^{76}As during its decay to ^{76}Se, which it does with a half-life of 26·7 hr. Equally, however, we could have monitored the prompt γ-rays emitted immediately after the neutron capture and in the de-excitation of ^{76}As to the ground state. This is, of course, more difficult, because these prompt γ-rays are emitted only during the neutron capture.* We see, therefore, that in the general case of a nucleus A being bombarded with neutrons, and neutron capture taking place to form a compound nucleus B with the emission of a prompt γ-ray during the de-excitation, we can write the reaction down as

$$A(n, \gamma)B.$$

Furthermore, we can monitor the prompt gamma-rays (γ) to determine the amount of A in the sample (this is called 'capture γ-ray analysis'), or we can monitor the radioactivity of the product nucleus B (this is called 'radioactivation analysis'). In some cases, the product nucleus formed is

* Strictly speaking within a time of 10^{-12} sec of the neutron capture.

stable, i.e. non-radioactive, and then the capture γ-ray method of analysis is the only method. It will be appreciated therefore that the two methods, capture γ-ray analysis and radio-activation analysis, are complementary techniques.

As an example we may consider the reaction

$$^{14}N(n, \gamma)^{15}N.$$

With ordinary nitrogen (^{14}N) bombarded with neutrons, neutron capture takes place and the product nucleus ^{15}N is formed. The nuclide ^{15}N is stable, i.e. non-radioactive. Hence, in this case monitoring the prompt γ-rays is the only method of analysis possible. This method has been applied to measuring the total nitrogen content of fertilisers, and since it can be extremely rapid, and takes no account of how the nitrogen is combined (it monitors, in fact, the total number of nitrogen nuclei in the sample), it can be a very valuable method.

NEUTRON GENERATORS

The most convenient method of generating neutrons, if a nuclear reactor is not available, is to bombard a tritium target (tritium is an isotope of hydrogen of atomic weight 3, and is represented by ^3H) with deuterium ions. Deuterium or heavy hydrogen has an atomic weight of 2 and is represented by ^2H. The following reaction takes place,

$$^3H(^2H, n)^4He,$$

producing the nucleus of a helium 4 atom, or to give it its more usual name, an α-particle, and a neutron is emitted. These generators can be operated continuously, producing a continuous output of neutrons. Alternatively, the ion beam can be pulsed, and the neutrons produced in bursts or pulses.

The neutrons from a neutron generator of this type are emitted in all directions, but in every case, if a neutron is emitted in one direction a corresponding α-particle is emitted in the reverse direction. This is necessary from momentum considerations. This phenomenon provides an excellent way of rejecting much of the background. A small α-particle detector is placed behind the neutron generator as shown in Fig. 46 so as to subtend a small defined solid angle. Thus, each signal in the α-detector defines a neutron in a similar solid angle. Therefore, by accepting only those signals from the α-particle detector, which are in coincidence* with signals

* The practically simultaneous production of signals from the two detectors.

from the γ-ray detector, only γ-rays which have travelled in a well-defined direction corresponding to the object to be irradiated are accepted. This leads to a reduction in the background by a factor of about 100 times with consequent improvement in the signal to noise ratio, i.e. the sensitivity of the system. It also endows the system with more precise locating characteristics.

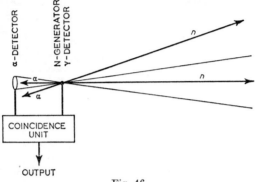

Fig. 46.

The idea may be extended still further by arranging a line of α-detectors behind the neutron generator and switching each successive detector into the circuit in turn. The beam can therefore be scanned up and down in the manner of a search radar. This is illustrated in Fig. 47. Furthermore, as already explained, the neutron beam may be pulsed and then the similarity with ordinary radar is more apparent.

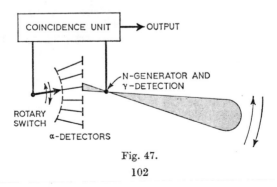

Fig. 47.

Capture γ-ray analysis has been used as already noted for a number of industrial applications. Obviously, the ideas of scanning could be applied to prospecting and the fact that the bombarding (n) and the emitted radiation (γ) are very penetrating makes the idea quite attractive. However, the most spectacular use that has been made is to determine the main constituents of the moon's crust. This involves landing an instrument package on the moon, the package comprising a miniature neutron generator giving an output of high-energy

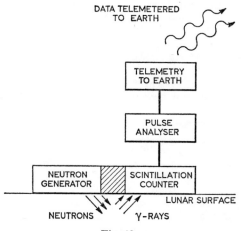

Fig. 48.

neutrons, a γ-ray detector, a pulse-amplitude analyser (spectrometer), and a read-out unit feeding into a telemetry unit system. This is illustrated in Fig. 48. Fortunately, neutron generators of small dimensions and adequate output are available. The neutron bombardment causes capture (n, γ) reactions, which have already been discussed, inelastic scattering (n, n', γ) reactions, in which a neutron with reduced energy as well as a γ-ray are emitted, and activation methods, in which the product nucleus formed is radioactive and may therefore be detected and identified by the radiations emitted.

These three different nuclear reactions can be sorted by suitable time discrimination. Thus, in the case of inelastic scattering the neutron de-excites promptly with the emission of a γ-ray. In the case of (n, γ) reactions, the neutron, if originally of high energy, has to be thermalised before capture, taking of the order of microseconds to milliseconds, whereas in the case of activation reactions, where the neutron is absorbed to form a new nucleus which is radioactive it decays with a characteristic half-life with the emission of γ-rays. It will be seen therefore that if all three types of nuclear reactions take place, the final result is a series of three independent γ-ray spectra, which can be sorted according to their time dependence. In practice, this time sorting is accomplished by pulsing the neutron source and gating* the γ-ray detecting system. The different elements are recognised by the energy spectra of the γ-emissions as already explained.

In practice, as the moon has no atmosphere, there will be the possibility of the system providing useful results before it actually lands on the moon's surface. Once a landing has been achieved the system will naturally respond with greater efficiency because of proximity and it should be possible to determine the chief elements which make up the moon's crust. One important problem to solve is whether the moon has a differentiated surface (as has the earth), or whether the surface is relatively undifferentiated. This can be determined by comparing the composition of the moon's crust with that of the earth and with that of relatively undifferentiated material, such as that from meteorites.

It should be noted that it is unnecessary to recover the instrument package from the moon, since the information is telemetered by radio back to the earth as it is obtained.

* Gating is a process of selecting those portions of a waveform during one or more selected time-intervals after the initiating pulse (i.e. the neutron pulse in this case).

CHAPTER TEN

MODERN RADAR

INTRODUCTION

Since World War II there have been many developments of radar. Some of these have been fairly conventional, such as the use of radar on marine craft to aid navigation and the use of c.w. radar for the determination of the speed of motor-cars to assist the police in their duties. Another interesting development is the use of 'wired radar' for finding faults on overhead transmission lines for the transmissions of electrical energy.

As radar is essentially a method of measuring distance, there have, of course, been many applications of radar to navigation, usually employing the principle of secondary radar with the aid of, say, a ground beacon, which can be interrogated with suitable apparatus in aircraft requiring a 'fix'. It is interesting to note that the need for greater and greater precision of distance measurement has naturally encouraged the use of shorter and shorter pulse lengths. One of the recent developments is a Subnanosecond Radar providing a pulse duration of 0·6 nanosec. This is capable of resolving as separate signals two rods 4 in. apart, and therefore opens up the way to conduct remote thickness measurements in the laboratory. As it provides distance measurement by the accurate measurement of very short time-intervals, it could also be useful for the evaluation of recovery times, the investigation of breakdown phenomena, relaxation times and other time-dependent microwave effects.

Radar has also invaded the field of the civil engineer, by providing the Tellurometer. This is a radar-type equipment which supplies the land surveyor with, effectively, an electronic measuring tape.

MILITARY RADARS AND THE ANTENNA

However, it is in radar as a system for the detection and tracking of missiles used for military purposes that the changes have been greatest. Radar systems today are over a million times more sensitive that they were a decade ago. To understand these improvements it is necessary to appreciate that the typical target in World War II was an aircraft with a reflecting cross-section of about 10 m². However, at the present time military targets are mostly missile warheads with a reflecting cross-section of the order of 0·1 m², which therefore calls for a considerable increase in sensitivity.

Apart from the reduction in the reflecting cross-section of targets of interest, it should be appreciated that missiles do attain considerable altitudes, much above the ceiling of the high-flying aircraft of World War II, and hence radars are required for missile targets which get high enough to appear in line of sight whilst upwards of 2000 miles away (see Fig. 49). This calls for a further increase of sensitivity. The signal received at the radar station is proportional to the reflecting

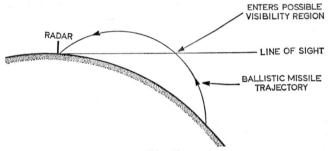

Fig. 49.

cross-section and is inversely proportional to the fourth power of the range. Hence the first factor (reduction of reflecting cross-section from 10 m² to 0·1 m²) requires a 100-fold increase in sensitivity, whereas the second factor (operation at a range of 2000 miles instead of 200 miles) requires a $10^4 = 10{,}000$-fold increase in sensitivity. It is apparent therefore that if the modern radar of today is giving this sort of performance, that it represents an improvement in sensitivity of about a million (10^6) times.

To understand how this improvement has been obtained the formula must be examined for sensitivity of a radar system, namely

$$\text{Sensitivity} = K_1 \times \frac{(\text{Antenna area} \times \text{frequency})^2}{(\text{Distance to target})^4}$$
$$\times \frac{\text{Transmitter power}}{\text{Receiver noise temperature}},$$

can be rewritten as

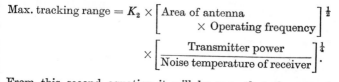

$$\text{Max. tracking range} = K_2 \times \left[\begin{array}{l}\text{Area of antenna}\\ \qquad \times \text{ Operating frequency}\end{array}\right]^{\frac{1}{2}}$$
$$\times \left[\frac{\text{Transmitter power}}{\text{Noise temperature of receiver}}\right]^{\frac{1}{4}}.$$

From this second equation it will be seen that the use of larger aerials and higher operating frequencies will pay the biggest dividends, but in fact the improvement has been obtained by a combination of improvements involving using very large aerial systems, very high operating frequencies, increases in the transmitted power and the use of special receivers with very low noise temperatures. Most of them have resulted from improvements along fairly conventional lines, but improvements concerning in some cases large-scale engineering have also been involved. Thus, in the case of the aerial system, these have gone up in size from the 30 ft by 10 ft systems used in World War II to 400 ft by 140 ft. Clearly, with an aerial system of these gigantic proportions, the mechanical movement of the aerial to provide direction-finding is impossible if the mechanical rigidity for accurate co-phasing of the aerial elements is to be maintained for the necessary preservation of the polar diagram, and so a fixed aerial system was adopted with electrical beam swinging. At one time we would have regarded the construction and maintenance of an antenna of these large dimensions with electrical beam swinging as impossible. The fact that it has become possible is largely because of the availability, after long development of high-frequency components of the necessary precision and stability and at relatively low prices. The principle of so-called phased arrays will be clear from Fig. 50. A number of small aerials are used each with its own receiver and transmitter. It will be apparent that if the individual units are operated so that the radar pulses reach all the aerials at the same instant of time, a parallel wavefront is launched from the face of the array, which radiates in a perpendicular direction. Clearly also the angular orientation of this array can be varied by introducing a linearly increasing time-delay into the arrival of the pulses at each of the aerials. Scanning and beam steering can therefore be controlled by the use of electronic circuits producing a regular switching pattern. This is the method used in 'search'. Once a target has been obtained a high-speed digital computer takes over and controls the orientation of the beam so that the target remains continuously in view.

To appreciate the magnitude of this engineering feat in producing aerials of this sort, it is worth giving a few figures. First, if an aerial beamwidth of 1° is required, an aerial aperture of 60 wavelengths is required. Second, all the individual components of the aerial must be spaced relatively close together. A spacing of about 0·6 of a wavelength is about the best to achieve the best compromise between the main beam directivity and freedom from the unwanted side lobes. Hence it follows that about 100 individual aerial elements are wanted altogether. However, we have mentioned only one dimension

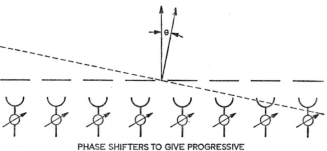

PHASE SHIFTERS TO GIVE PROGRESSIVE
CHANGE OF PHASE ACROSS THE ARRAY

Fig. 50.

and our beam must not only be 1° wide in azimuth but 1° wide in elevation as well, so that the generation of the necessary pencil beam 1° × 1° requires a matrix of 100 aerial elements by 100 aerial elements, i.e. 10,000 aerial elements altogether.

It should be noted that the successful construction of this gigantic aerial array not only solves the aerial problem, but the transmitter problem as well, because it is now possible to transmit many megawatts of power, since the combined power output of the system is the sum of the power outputs of the various individual elements. It is, however, essential that the individual aerial elements should be accurately co-phased, and means be available for introducing, when required, the necessary time-delays into the arrival of the pulses at each of the elements. Moreover, it is absolutely necessary that the system should be reliable and have good stability. This is what has been achieved.

It is probably worth mentioning that during World War II Britain used aerials comprising a parabolic reflector with a small dipole aerial at the focus. If this method had been adopted for the military radars, undoubtedly beamwidths of 1° could have been achieved, but the large mechanical size and weight of the aerial structure would have introduced large mechanical inertia, and it would have been impossible to steer the beam precisely and with the necessary speed. There would also have been the difficult problem of feeding the very large power to a single dipole, a problem which is avoided with the co-phased aerial array system.

THE TRANSMITTER

During and after World War II the magnetron was undoubtedly in a special position as a generator of radar waves, but with the need for greater ranges and ability to detect targets of small reflecting cross-section, the preferred system now is to produce a coherent transmitted waveform employing a series of amplifier stages to build up a signal waveform from a low level to an appropriate power for feeding into an antenna system. This has given special emphasis to the development of amplifier tubes with both high gain* and efficiency. Tetrodes and klystrons are used for this purpose. A klystron is an electron tube which employs velocity modulation to generate or amplify electromagnetic energy in the microwave region. The two-cavity tube is often employed, both cavities being tuned to the same frequency, the input being applied to the first cavity where bunching of the electrons emitted by a cathode takes place, and the output being taken from a second cavity (designated the catcher cavity) connected to the first both mechanically and electrically.

The direct current (i.e. the beam current from the cathode) is therefore converted into radio-frequency energies. Some tubes of this type have additional cavities and may be upwards of 11 ft long. Gains can be as high as 10,000 times and the efficiency of the order of 35%. Tremendous achievements have been obtained in recent years by optimising the various parameters involved in the design of klystrons and increases in the power output of upwards of 100 times have been achieved.

* In this context 'gain' means the ratio of the output signal to the input signal.

For microwave systems it is usual to employ the concept of noise temperature. In considering the noise temperature of a radar system the various contributing factors relevant to low system performance must be considered. These are (i) the input noise temperature of the receiver; (ii) the component effects; and (iii) the aerial noise including the effect of any side lobe pick-up. Some years ago the best receivers available

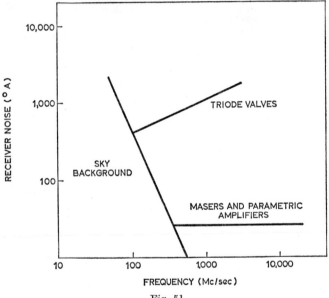

Fig. 51.

operating in the microwave band had an equivalent noise temperature of about 3000° K (see Fig. 51 for details of how the noise temperature depends on frequency). In the past two years helium-cooled masers* have made their appearance

* This is a contraction for microwave amplification by stimulated emission of radiation. The term describes the general class of microwave amplification based on molecular interaction with electromagnetic radiation. They convert the internal energy of the molecular system into microwave energy by the interaction of electromagnetic energy directly with the molecular system.

with an equivalent noise temperature of only 20° K. If the aerial system is looking into the cold sky instead of at the 290° K of the earth's surface, the effective noise temperature of the system (sky noise, aerial noise and receiver noise) can be less than 100° K,* which therefore gives a 30-fold improvement (as compared with the 3000° K for the conventional system). This can be compared with the increase in sensitivity, which would be obtained by an increase in transmitter power which would be by 30 times.

SIGNAL PROCESSING EQUIPMENT

Perhaps the most spectacular change which has been made to radar systems since World War II is in connection with the signal processing and control functions of these stations. In the early days of radar it was satisfactory for an operator to sit in front of the cathode-ray tube display and take actions manually as a result of the information presented on the cathode-ray tube. The high speed of present-day missiles and the needs of anti-missile defence have called for many changes. First, the human operator now acts only as a monitor for the operation to ensure that the correct action is taken in the event of anything unforeseen taking place, otherwise the operation is entirely automatic. The signal-processing equipment sorts through the radar data, applying filtering and correlation tests at a much higher speed than could be attempted by a human operator. Thus, in deciding whether radar output data qualifies as a target of interest, information is stored and brought forward at a later stage for comparison with more recent radar data. Furthermore, if a target fails, the computer can take charge of the aerial orientation on the basis of extrapolation of old data on the target of interest from the memory, until such time as the target is re-sighted and properly identified.

The signal-processing equipment associated with a modern radar station is exceedingly complex and costly, and would never have been possible without the development of the

---

* It may be noted that this figure of 100° K does not represent the limit. For example, the sky temperature at the zenith is always very much less than at only a few degrees elevation. Similarly the subsidiary side-lobe effect may correspond to only 2° K at zenith, whereas a typical figure would be 30° K near the elevation. Hence for applications involving orientations near the zenith the total effective noise temperature may be as low as 10° K.

111

transistor and the improvement in component reliability which its use allows. It should be appreciated that with an equipment comprising a million (10^6) or so components, very high reliability of individual components is required, if any reasonable life (i.e. time between successive faults) is to be obtained. Fortunately, the advent of the transistor has allowed this and even with equipments involving of the order of 10^6 components a life approaching a year between successive faults can be obtained, and with satisfactory built-in test facilities, the amount of 'out-time' in the case of an actual fault occurring can be made very small. This involves the use of routine tests which are carried out at regular intervals and any units which exhibit a change of characteristics (and which may therefore fail in the future) are replaced. Furthermore, the signal-processing equipment itself is designed to be an assembly of a large number of standard units, the numbers of variants of these units being as small as possible. This obviously aids maintenance by replacing a faulty unit by an equivalent unit.

APPENDIX 1

BOOKS FOR FURTHER READING

1. RADAR

TAYLOR, D. and WESTCOTT, C. H. *Principles of Radar*. Cambridge University Press, 1948.

ROWE, A. P. *One Story of Radar*. Cambridge University Press, 1948.

BOULDING, R. S. H. *Principles and Practice of Radar*. Geo. Newnes Ltd., 1963.

SIR ROBERT WATSON-WATT, *Three Steps to Victory*. Odhams, 1957.

2. AIDS TO NAVIGATION

SMITH, R. A. *Radio Aids to Navigation*. Cambridge University Press, 1947.

3. RADIO ASTRONOMY

JENNISON, R. C. *Radio Astronomy*. Geo. Newnes Ltd. (In the press —a companion volume to the present book.)

PAWSEY, J. L. and BRACEWELL, R. N. *Radio Astronomy*. Oxford University Press, 1955.

4. RADIOSPECTROSCOPY

INGRAM, D. J. E. *Spectroscopy at Radio and Microwave Frequencies*. Butterworths Scientific Publications, 1959.

SQUIRES, T. L. *Introduction to Microwave Spectroscopy*. Geo. Newnes Ltd., 1963.

5. RADIOACTIVATION ANALYSIS

TAYLOR, D. *Neutron Irradiation and Activation Analysis*. Geo. Newnes Ltd., 1963.

6. MODERN AND CIVIL RADAR

SKOLNIK, M. R. *Introduction to Radar Ssytems*. McGraw-Hill Book Co., 1962.

OVERHAGE, C. F. J. Chapter 4 of the *Age of Electronics*. McGraw-Hill Book Co., 1962.

GLOSSARY OF TERMS

Type A display. This is the type of presentation on a cathode-ray oscilloscope in which time is one co-ordinate and signals appear as deflections in a direction perpendicular to the time-scale.

Accelerator is a machine designed to impart large kinetic energy to charged particles such as electrons, protons, etc.

A.C.R. is a contraction for 'airfield control radar', which is radar equipment for observing the movement of aircraft in the vicinity of an airfield.

Activation is usually defined as the process of inducing radioactivity, and in the context in which the term is used in the present book, the production of radionuclides by neutron bombardment.

An activation reaction is a nuclear reaction in which the product formed is radioactive. There are many such reactions which may be induced by bombarding ordinary materials with neutrons. Thus ordinary sodium (^{23}Na) when bombarded with thermal neutrons forms a radioactive form of sodium (^{24}Na), which decays by negative β-particle emission and γ-ray emission with a half-life of 14·8 hr to form magnesium (^{24}Mg) which is stable, i.e. non-radioactive.

Adcock antenna. This is a system comprising two vertical antennas separated by a distance of one-half wavelength or less and connected in phase opposition to produce a directional pattern having the shape of a figure eight.

An aerial is an exposed wire capable of radiating or receiving the energy to or from electromagnetic waves.

A.I. is a contraction for 'air interception' and refers to the airborne radar equipment used for effecting interception of hostile aircraft.

A.I./B.A. (see B.A.B.S.). This refers to the use of the B.A.B.S system with A.I.

Alpha (α)-particle is a fast-moving helium (^{4}He) nucleus, i.e. a particle having a mass of four and a charge of two units. Certain radioactive materials decay by the emission of α-particles.

Amplitude modulation is modulation in which the amplitude of the wave is the characteristic varied.

Anomalous propagation is characterised by the formation of a 'duct' close to the earth's surface, in which the radio waves are trapped as if in a waveguide. Just as in a conventional waveguide there is a critical wavelength above which propagation along the guide does not occur, so that the duct can only trap energy if the wavelength is short enough—longer waves behave relatively normally. The result of the formation of such a duct is that the field strength close to the earth attenuates much more slowly than under orthodox conditions, and the horizon ceases to provide any limitation at all. In the tropics, cases have been authenticated of radar ranges being received from ranges well above 1000 miles, due to duct conditions.

An antenna is a system of conductors used for the transmission and/or reception of electromagnetic waves. It is usually applied to aerial systems with specified characteristics.

A.S.V. is a contraction for 'air to surface vessels', and is the airborne radar equipment used for the detection of ships, surfaced submarines, etc.

B.A.B.S. is a contraction for 'beam approach beacon system' and is a system of instrument landing using radar beacons and interrogators.

Bandwidth of a device is the difference between the limiting frequencies within which performance in respect to some characteristic falls within specified limits.

Beam system is a radio system in which highly directive transmitting and receiving aerials are employed.

Beta (β)-particle is an electron ejected from the nucleus during the decay of a radionuclide, the electrons carrying a positive or a negative charge and being designated positive or negative β-particles.

Betatron is a type of accelerator, in which electrons are accelerated by means of magnetic induction.

Broadside antenna is an antenna array usually comprising a number of half-wave aerials driven in-phase, all the elements being physically in the same plane. Such an array has its direction of maximum radiation (when used for transmitting) perpendicular to the plane of the array.

Capture gamma rays are the instantaneous γ-rays resulting from radiative capture. In this volume we are particularly interested in the capture by the bombarded nuclei of neutrons, and so the capture γ-rays are the γ-rays emitted immediately following neutron capture.

C.H. is a contraction for 'chain home', which refers to the early warning radars operating on a wavelength of about 10 m.

C.H.L. is a contraction for 'chain home low', and refers to the early warning radars operating on a wavelength of 1·5 m and specifically designed for detecting low-flying aircraft.

Collision warning radars are airborne radar equipment for providing information about other aircraft in the vicinity in such a way that collisions can be avoided.

Compton scattering is the reduction of energy of a γ-photon by its interaction with a free or loosely bound electron, by which process a part of the energy is transferred to the electron and a part remains with the photon which is thereby redirected with reduced energy.

Counting-rate meter is an instrument which gives a continuous indication of the average rate of arrival of pulses from a counter.

C.R.O. is a contraction for cathode-ray oscilloscope.

Cross-section of a given nucleus or atom for a given radiation is that area perpendicular to the direction of the radiation which has to be attributed to the nucleus or atom to account geometrically for its interaction with the radiation.

c.w. is a contraction for continuous wave and in the strict sense of the word refers to continuous unmodulated transmissions of a single carrier frequency. However, it is sometimes used to refer to continuous transmissions even though carrying simple modulations, in order to distinguish from pulse transmissions.

Decibel is a dimensionless unit for expressing the ratio of two values of the power, the number of decibels being 10 times the logarithm to the base 10 of the power ratio. It is abbreviated to dB.

Deuterium is the special name given to heavy hydrogen (^{2}H), i.e. hydrogen with a mass of two units.

d.f. is direction finding.

Doppler effect is the apparent change in the frequency of vibrations, such as those of sound, light and radio waves when the source and the observer are in relative motion to one another.

Doppler system. In radar, this is any system utilising the Doppler effect for obtaining information, e.g. velocity of target being observed.

Echoing area is that part of a radar target that effectively returns echoes to the radar set.

Electron is the negatively charged particle which forms a common constituent of all atoms. There is a positively charged counterpart of equal mass and charge, which is called a positive electron or a positron. Sometimes the negatively charged electron is called a negatron.

Fast neutrons are neutrons having appreciable energy, usually above 0·1 MeV.

Floodlighting systems. The early radars were of this type, a transmitting antenna being employed to 'floodlight' a wide area in front of the station, and a receiving antenna is used for direction-finding.

Fourier analysis is a method of mathematical or physical analysis of a periodic wave function leading to its component harmonic functions. Thus, in considering the usual form of pulsed radar, it may be noted that the modulation waveform is periodic with a fundamental frequency f_p say, so that its spectrum must consist of a number of harmonics of this frequency. Since the pulse length τ is usually much smaller than the pulse interval $1/f_p$, it may be shown that much of the energy will be in the region of very high harmonics, having frequencies of the order of $1/\tau$.

Frequency modulation (f.m.) is modulation in which the frequency of the wave is the characteristic varied.

Gamma radiation (i.e. γ-rays) is electromagnetic radiation of very short wavelength emitted by atomic nuclei.

G.C.A. is a contraction for 'ground controlled approach' and is an extremely high-precision microwave radar equipment which gives the position of the aircraft in terms of its range, azimuth and elevation. By this means the position of the aircraft relative to a predetermined approach path is displayed on the ground and a controller gives the aircraft landing instructions and 'talks it down'.

Gee is a radar navigational system operating in the v.h.f. band, based on the measurement of time-differences and thus laying down a hyperbolic lattice.

G.L. is a contraction for 'gun laying' and is the radar equipment for providing information to the guns to allow them to lay on to the target.

G.H. is a high-precision navigational aid based on accurate measurement of range and used for aerial survey and blind bombing.

Glide path is a radio beam in the form of an inclined plane extending upwards at an angle to the horizontal from the point of desired landing.

Goniometer is a system of two coils which are arranged geometrically to provide a field distribution so that the orientation of a third coil is proportional to their respective field strengths.

Ground clutter. This is the pattern produced on the screen of a radar C.R.O. by undesired ground returns.

Half-life of a radionuclide is the time required for the radioactivity to decay to half its initial value. Note that after twice this period (i.e. $2t_{\frac{1}{2}}$) only a quarter of the activity remains. After a time $nt_{\frac{1}{2}}$ the activity remaining is $(\frac{1}{2})^n$ of the original activity.

H_2S is a contraction for 'Home Sweet Home', and is a microwave radar equipment which provides a radar map of the country over which the aircraft is flying.

I.F.F. is a contraction for 'identification, friend or foe', and is a system for identifying friendly aircraft by means of radar.

I.L.S. is a contraction for 'instrument landing system'.

Inelastic scattering is scattering in which the struck nucleus is excited, or broken up, or captures the incoming particle.

Interferometer is an apparatus used to produce or show interference between two or more wavetrains coming from the same emitting area.

Ionosphere is that region above the earth's surface in which ionisation takes place, with diurnal and annual variations which are regularly associated with the ultraviolet light from the sun, and sporadic variations arising from hydrogen bursts from sunspots. Layers or regions possessing defined characteristics, which are important in radio propagation are known as the E and F layers.

Isotopes are nuclides having the same atomic number (number of units of charge on the nucleus), but different mass numbers.

Klystron is an electron tube which employs velocity modulation to generate or amplify electromagnetic energy in the microwave region.

Loran is a navigational system developed in the U.S.A. using the same principle as Gee, but operating originally on a frequency near to 2 Mc/sec.

Magnetron is a high-vacuum thermionic tube capable of producing high-output power in the microwave region of the frequency spectrum. It comprises a heater, cathode, a multi-segment anode in the form of a number of resonant cavities and an external magnet for control purposes.

Maser is a contraction for 'microwave amplification by stimulated emission of radiation', and the term describes the general class of microwave amplifiers based on molecular interaction with electro-magnetic radiation.

Matching is the connecting and adjusting of two circuits in such a way that the impedances are of such a value as to insure that maximum transfer of energy exists in the circuits.

Matching stub is a method of impedance-matching employing stubs to effect maximum energy transfer in transmission lines.

m.f. refers to a band of frequencies extending from 300 kc/sec to 3 Mc/sec.

Microwave spectroscopy is that branch of spectroscopy concerned with the method and techniques of observing and interpreting the absorption and emission of electromagnetic radiation at microwave frequencies by matter—solids, liquids and gases.

Modulation is the process or the result of the process whereby some characteristic of one wave is varied in accordance with some characteristic of another.

Neutron is a particle of zero charge and very slightly heavier than a proton.

Noise factor of a receiver is a factor which measures how much worse the receiver is than the theoretical minimum which is set by the Johnson effect.

Noise temperature is the temperature of a passive system having the available noise power per unit bandwidth equal to that of the actual terminals of the device under consideration. Thus, the noise temperature of a simple resistor is the actual temperature of the resistor, whereas the noise temperature of a diode may be many times the observed absolute temperature. This concept of noise temperature is used in considering the performance of radar equip-ments. At wavelengths greater than about 20 m, receivers are readily available which generate less noise than is picked up by even a quite inefficient aerial. The background noise determines the limit of perceptible signals, and improvement of the aerial increases both signal and noise in the same ratio, so that no advantage is gained by having an efficient receiving aerial. For shorter wave-lengths the situation is quite different; the limit of sensitivity is set by noise generated in the receiver itself. Any improvement in aerial performance then gives an increase in the ratio of signal to noise and is therefore worthwhile. It should also be noted that for short wavelengths it is essential that receiving aerials, as well as transmitting aerials, should work at maximum efficiency.

Nuclear reactor is a structure in which a fission chain reaction can be maintained and controlled. It will usually contain a fuel, coolant and moderator and is most often surrounded by a concrete biological shield to absorb neutron and γ-ray emission.

Nuclide is a species of atom characterised by its mass number, atomic number and nuclear energy state.

Oboe is a high-precision radar blind-bombing equipment, based on accurate range measurement.

Parametric amplifier is a low-noise, high-frequency amplifier that employs non-linear variation of capacitance or inductance to achieve amplification. The most common type is the back-biased silicon diode type, whose capacitance is varied by the application of microwave frequency power. As a low-noise, high-frequency amplifier the parametric amplifier competes with the maser. The maser has excellent performance with respect to noise, but it must be refrigerated to temperatures usually less than $4°$ C above absolute zero, and requires a strong and uniform magnetic field. Compared to the maser, therefore, the parametric amplifier is relatively simple.

Photoelectric effect is the complete absorption of a photon by an atom with the emission of an orbital electron.

Polar diagram. In the context used in the present book this is antenna polar diagram which is a cross-section of the radiation pattern of the antenna.

Polarisation. In the context used in the present book this is antenna polarisation, which is a term applied to the polarisation of the electromagnetic wave with particular reference to the radiation pattern of the antenna. The term 'polarisation' describes the variation of the electric field vector in any electromagnetic wave. In general, a vertical antenna produces vertically polarised waves, while horizontal antennas produce horizontally polarised waves. Linear receiving antennas must lie in the direction of the polarisation, to receive maximum power.

Positron is a positively charged electron, which is the antiparticle of the ordinary electron (the negatron). Certain radioactive materials decay by the emission of high-speed electrons (negatrons) and some by the emission of high-speed positrons.

P.P.I. is a contraction for 'plan position indicator', which is a cathode-ray tube display for the 'map' type.

Pulse amplifier is an electronic amplifier designed to amplify and often to shape pulses from a radiation detector.

Pulse height analyser is an instrument incorporating a pulse height selector (see later) in which the channel width is pre-set and the threshold varied either manually or automatically to scan the amplitude spectrum of the incoming pulses.

Pulse height discriminator is an electronic circuit which accepts only those pulses having amplitudes greater than a pre-set level and produces an output pulse of fixed amplitude for each input pulse accepted.

Pulse height selector is an electronic circuit which permits only those pulses having amplitudes between predetermined levels to be passed to the succeeding circuits. The difference between these levels is the channel width, and the lower reference level is the threshold.

Pulse modulation is modulation of the carrier by pulses.

Radar has been defined in the introduction as 'the science of locating distant objects by radio'. However, the more exact definition of radar is a system for measuring at least two of the co-ordinates which define the position of an object with respect to an observer, one of these co-ordinates being the distance between them and is inferred directly from the time of travel of a radio wave travelling by the shortest path between them. It is usual also to distinguish between primary radar, where the object to be located plays the purely passive part of reflecting a radio wave, secondary radar in which a responder is used to provide the return signal, and radio navigation in which, in principle, no return signal is necessary.

Radio altimeter (sometimes 'radar altimeter') is an altimeter which indicates the true altitude of an aircraft by measuring the time-interval for a radio-frequency pulse to travel from the aircraft to the ground and back to the aircraft, or the equivalent f.m. method.

Radio astronomy is the study of astronomical bodies by observing the radio waves they emit. This is a valuable supplement to the ordinary optical methods of investigations used in astronomy.

Range-elevation display is a type of cathode-ray tube display which indicates the height of a target as seen by a radar employing vertical scanning.

Reflection coefficients of the ground. A major consideration for many radar ground and ship equipments is the effect on the vertical polar diagram and gain of the existence of reflected radiation from the land or sea in front of the aerials. For one thing this radiation makes it impossible to obtain good field strengths at low angles of elevation without using aerials many wavelengths above the earth's surface—a severe limitation at long wavelengths. At sufficiently high frequencies (roughly about 100 Mc/sec for land and 2500 Mc/sec for sea) the electrical conductivity ceases to have any appreciable effect on the refractive index (μ), and is given by the simple formula $\mu = \sqrt{K}$, where K is the dielectric constant (about 10 for ground and 80 for sea water).

Refractive index of atmosphere. The refractive index of the atmosphere depends on its density and humidity. The refractive index (μ) for any frequency within the usual radar band is given by

$$\mu - 1 = \frac{80}{T}\left(\times 10^{-6}\, p + \frac{4800}{T}\, W \right),$$

where p is the atmosphere pressure in millibars, W is the partial pressure of water vapour in millibars, and T is the absolute temperature (°K). The absolute value of this index is only required when very accurate ranging is necessary. For normal purposes it is the bending of the rays due to gradients of refractive index which is more important.

Responder. This is an equipment, which when triggered by the reception of a pulse signal from a radar transmitter, generates a second pulse which is transmitted by the responder. Such a responder can generate much more energy than would be returned by simple reflection from the target.

S.B.A. is a contraction for 'standard beam approach', and is an instrument-landing system developed from the Lorentz system and presenting information as aural dots and dashes.

Scaler is an electronic circuit used for counting purposes, e.g. of the number of particles reaching a counter.

Sea clutter is the pattern produced on the screen of a radar C.R.O. by undesired sea returns which renders the observation of ship targets difficult or impossible.

Secondary radar is the radar system which depends on the use of a responder in the target (or targets) to be followed. Such a system can provide stronger signals and freedom from clutter.

Side lobe is a portion of the radiation from an antenna outside the main beam and usually of much smaller intensity.

Synchrotron is a device for accelerating particles (e.g. electrons) in a circular orbit in an increasing magnetic field by means of an alternating electric field applied in synchronism with the orbital motion.

Thermal neutrons are neutrons in approximate thermal equilibrium with their moderator. Their mean energy is then about 0·025 eV, and their mean velocity about 2200 m/sec, which is quite slow compared with fast neutrons.

Time-base is a bright line on the cathode-ray screen traced by the electron beam in synchronism with the transmitted pulses, by which range of a target is determined as a function of time as indicated by the distance of the echo signal along the line.

T.R.E. is a contraction for the Telecommunications Research Establishment, Malvern, the wartime radar research establishment of the Ministry of Aircraft Production. It is now under the Ministry of Aviation and has been renamed the Royal Radar Establishment (R.R.E.).

T.R. switch is an automatic device employed in radar for allowing a single aerial to be employed both for transmitting and receiving. During the transmitter pulse the aerial is connected to the transmitter and the receiver is isolated. After the transmitter pulse the transmitter is isolated and the receiver is connected to the aerial.

Tritium is an isotope of hydrogen having a mass number of 3.

Variable elevation beam (V.E.B.) radar is a radar system used for height-finding in which a beam, narrow in the vertical plane, is caused to scan up and down, and the information is presented on a range-elevation display.

v.h.f. is a contraction for 'very high frequency' and generally refers to a band of frequencies extending from 30 to 300 Mc/sec.

Waveguide comprises a hollow conducting tube within which electromagnetic waves may be propagated, or a solid dielectric or a dielectric-filled conductor for the same purpose. There are two common forms, namely, hollow cylindrical tubes and tubes with a rectangular cross-section. Radar systems generally use rectangular waveguides with dimensions so chosen that only one dominant mode is propagated.

w.t. is a contraction for 'wireless telegraphy', usually of Morse code signals.

INDEX*

* This Index should be used in conjunction with the ' Glossary of Terms ' (Appendix 2).